In her thoughtful book, Debra guides
heartfelt help as we navigate the chang
because of a caregiving situation. I recommend this book to anyone
caring for a family member who wants answers to difficult
questions.

Denise M. Brown,
Founder, CareGiving.com

Author Debra Hallisey shares deeply personal feelings and
encounters in her own caregiving journey. I applaud her for that and
predict many readers will identify with, and be helped by, her
experiences. She went beyond personal stories to provide readers
with a variety of useful tips and tricks. This is the sort of guide that
everyone will return to often.

Glenna Crooke, Ph.D.
The Network Sage: Realize Your Network Superpower

This is a beautifully and thoughtfully written book. The idea of a
caregiver relationship contract is genius and helps the reader to
understand that what's happening really is a sort of contract, and
that both people can work together to make that relationship easier
even in the face of life-changing circumstances.

Danielle L. Kunkle
Boomer Benefits

She skillfully defines the caregiver 'dance' in a way that brings
clarity and insights in a time that is often confusing. The book is
infused with therapeutic wisdom and practical exercises that will
help you build a stronger caregiver tool kit.

Annette Murphy, MSW, LSW
Director of Home Care and Care Management
Springpoint at Home

This book has clear, real life examples of the successes and
frustrations of caregiving, as well as the joys. Valuable information
and insights are offered to guide us through difficult conversations,
asking for help, and dealing with emotions. Debra outlines the
importance of respectfully including our parents in the decision-
making process, which can lead to a smoother path. Debra shows

how caregiving can be a time of shared joy and result in a more satisfying, supportive relationship based on mutual respect. Her Deb's life-giving approach with her own mother can help us to honor our role as a caregiver, while reminding us the importance of nurturing ourselves along the way.

Hillary Murray
Director of Community Relations
Brandywine Living at Pennington

Caregiving is more than just a series of tasks to keep your loved one safe. Debra Hallisey takes us on a wise and practical journey through some of the hardest conversations you will ever have in your life. She uses her experience to show us the importance of truly connecting, while always showing your parents the respect they deserve. This is the book every person with aging parents needs to read before the crisis hits. This is the book that will shed some light on the darkest of days and will help you create the caregiver contract that will restore the quality of life that you and your loved one both need and provide clarity and insight to your caregiving relationship.

Sheli Monacchio, President
Caring Connections of New Jersey

This book is a wonderful guide through a difficult maze of parent-child-parent relationships. Through organized lists and informational anecdotes, Ms. Hallisey acquaints the reader with the necessary considerations when taking on the care of a loved one. Everyone with a parent should read this, and every parent should gift their child with a copy!

Susan R. Ferraro

Your Caregiver Relationship Contract

How to navigate the minefield of new roles and expectations

Debra Hallisey

Your Caregiver Relationship Contract
How to navigate the minefield of new roles and expectations

Published by
Advocate for Mom and Dad, LLC
Box 55340
2601 Brunswick Pike
Lawrenceville, NJ 08638

Cover design by Eric Labacz, www.labaczdesign.com

This book is dedicated to the millions of family caregivers who quietly, with grace and humor, care for their loved ones.

Mom made me promise I wouldn't dedicate this book to her, so I won't. But I will thank her for her generosity in letting me tell our caregiving story. Mom's willingness to step out of her comfort zone and co-create a new relationship contract with me has brought us to a new and better understanding of one another and forged an unbreakable team.

I am also thankful to family, friends, and clients who willingly share their stories with me and, in doing so, let me be their voice. Such honesty and vulnerability humble me. This book would not be possible without you. Because of your insights, I educate other family caregivers and help them find the resources they need. I can assure other family caregivers they are not alone on this journey—for we indeed have each other's back.

I am thankful to the eldercare professionals I have met since starting Advocate for Mom and Dad, LLC. They care so deeply for the people they serve, have been unfailingly gracious about sharing what they know, and are willing to help everyone navigate the steep learning curve of our healthcare system. My work and this book would not be possible without them.

To the friends and family who understood when I seemed to have dropped off the face of the earth while writing this book, thank you. You love me anyway, continue to support me, and occasionally convince me to leave the office and come out to play. You will never know how much I need you.

My thank you would be incomplete without mentioning my writing coach and publisher Karen Miller of Open Door Publications and Eric Labacz of Eric Labacz Design for his beautiful book cover. A special thanks to my creative team Roberta Kearney and Michelle Seitzer, who kept me honest and helped make this book the best possible through their insights and comments. All opinions and any mistakes are mine.

Table of Contents

Introduction 1

1. What Is Your Caregiver Contract?.........................4
2. Life Changes for Everyone................................19
3. An Emotional Journey 36
4. Having Hard Conversations..............................51
5. Understanding Expectations and Setting Boundaries 64
6. Ask for and Say "YES" to Help 81
7. Your Caregiving Support Peeps...........................92
8. Everyone in Your Life Is Affected 104
   Conclusion 126
   Resources 128
   About the Author 138

Introduction

"You've learned so much, you should find a way to share it with people."

My mother, with this simple statement, started me down a path I never expected to take, one that has profoundly changed my life. Because of her suggestion, I founded Advocate for Mom and Dad. Starting my business, I began an ongoing blog on caregiving for adult children of aging parents at advocateformomanddad.com. I then became a Certified Caregiving Consultant™, working with family caregivers to find resources to relieve their top three stresses. And now I am providing this book, "Your Caregiver Relationship Contract: How to navigate the minefield of new roles and expectations."

I became a caregiver the year my father was diagnosed with congestive heart failure. Rather, I should say, I identified myself as a caregiver when Dad was diagnosed. I am currently and have been for five years my mother's caregiver. She is legally blind with mobility issues but otherwise is in good health.

Being a caregiver is hard work.

I don't mean the physical work of helping your loved one shower or dress. I mean the mental and emotional work it takes to be a caregiver. Over the last five years, I have met countless caregivers who told me their story. Each generously shared the resources they discovered. Without them my mother and I would not have a care plan that allows my mom to stay in her home. And I would not have started Advocate for Mom and Dad.

During the last five years I have learned lessons I want to share with you. The most important one is that becoming Mom's caregiver changed our mother/daughter relationship, our "contract," if you will. This idea of a relationship contract resounded with my clients and readers of my blog. Because it helps us to recognize there IS an unspoken contract, while inviting caregivers to do the hard-intentional work to co-create a new one.

Every family's caregiving journey is unique because each family is unique. My life has always been intertwined with my parents, whether I lived across the country or an hour away. Our family abounds with strong ties to our large Irish and Italian extended family, involving decades of social interaction. My mom still has deep roots in the local community.

But not every family is still intact. Not every family lives in close proximity to their family of origin, nor have they maintained close family ties.

Regardless of how your family story is written, as caregivers we face the same issues. How do you have the hard conversations? How do you deal with all the emotions that surface? What is the best way to deal with the expectations of other people and set needed boundaries? How do I say "yes" to help, ask for help, and get my loved one to buy into help? How can I build a support system that is just for me, the caregiver?

This book is written from my point of view as an adult child who cares for an aging parent. But the worksheets and example conversation starters at the end of every chapter will help you to co-create a caregiver relationship contract, even if the person you are caring for is a spouse, child, other family member, or friend. This book and the tools in it are designed to help you in your caregiver role, whether you live near or far, and it will help you if your role is to support someone who is a caregiver.

One final thought: I've always looked at relationships as a dance. If one partner changes the dance, the other has no option but to adapt or stop dancing. It is an analogy that works for negotiating a new caregiver relationship contract as well. In those hard conversations, in setting boundaries, in asking for help, you will change the dance you have been engaged in for years. My hope is that the ideas and tools found here keep you dancing in new, different, and better ways.

"The only way to make sense out of change is to plunge into it, move with it, and join the dance."

Alan Watts

Chapter 1
What is Your Caregiver Contract?

Every relationship is a contract. I don't mean a formal written contract. I mean the informal and often unspoken ways in which people agree to be in a relationship. What are we willing to do—or not do—for one another? How do we support one another? What are the social outlets and shared interests that bind your relationship together? These and other questions help to define the interactions and expectations for each relationship, in other words, the "contract."

Throughout this book we'll explore each of these questions. Using worksheets and exercises, we'll help you start to identify the tasks, rituals, and expectations that need to change in your relationship contract as you become a caregiver to your parent, your spouse, or another loved one. We will explore the question of how you can make these changes in a loving and supportive way.

This book is about changing your relationship contract with your loved one when you become their caregiver. This is very different from a family caregiver agreement. A family caregiver agreement is a term used by attorneys to describe a legal document that is essentially an employment contract between you (the family member) and your care recipient. If you have left a job or dropped down to half time work to care for an aging parent, it is possible to get paid as a caregiver. Be aware that getting paid to care for your loved one requires documenting hours worked, the type of caregiver services performed, the number of hours spent in caregiving, and withholding appropriate income tax and employer taxes.

"Family caregiver contracts must be able to stand up as a third-party contract, that is, it must be written as if the caregiver is someone unknown to the family, and the contract must be fair and reasonable considering all the circumstances," says Fiona Van Dyck Elder, founding member of the National Elder Law Foundation.

Unlike a caregiver **relationship** contract, a **family caregiver contract** has an impact on long term care planning for Medicaid. It is essential to work with an elder law or estate planning attorney and not try to create a family caregiver contract on your own.

How relationship contracts are formed

Relationship contracts are not legal documents. They are unwritten, emotional rules. It takes time to co-create a relationship contract. For example, my parents were married for 61 years. The contract they forged began when they started dating at age 16 through 61 years of marriage.

Think about all the relationships you have in your life. You are a child of someone, or you wouldn't be reading this book. But you may also be a spouse or a partner of someone, a parent, a friend, an aunt or uncle. All of these relationships have their own unwritten rules—their own "contracts."

In my parents' case, the contract they had so carefully developed was suddenly gone upon my father's death. Not only did Mom lose his companionship, she lost her way of being in the world. Her contract with my father included everything from who washed the dinner dishes to who took out the garbage, to what television shows were watched. On top of the emotional loss of her husband and the loving relationship they had shared, she had to adjust to a new caregiver—me, her daughter. Suddenly, our roles were if not completely reversed, at least in need of adjustment. And although our relationship had been adjusting slowly and consistently throughout the years from the time I left home and became an adult, this was a new, more drastic change. Our mother/daughter contract needed to adjust to our changing needs as well.

Changing a relationship contract takes self-awareness and work, but the end result is a stronger and deeper relationship. This makes it well worth the effort.

What are we willing to do (or not do) for one another?

If the person you are caring for is your husband or wife, you may have had a traditional relationship, such as my parents had, or a more modern one in which duties are shared equally, or at least in less conventional ways. Either way, when someone becomes ill and needs caregiving, the contract you had before, the dance, if you will, is changed.

Relationship contracts have both physical and emotional components. It's easy to identify physical tasks. One person like my dad takes care of finances. One person goes grocery shopping because the other hates it. The other puts groceries away, and together they cook dinner.

It often appears that people argue about physical tasks the most, such as not taking a turn picking up children from sports events or never doing the laundry. When, in reality, the argument is fueled because one person feels underappreciated or a task they hated in childhood is still being thrust upon their shoulders. We need to be aware of and willing to work on the underlying emotions that fuel an argument.

During their years together my parents' contract adjusted to the different stages in their life, but some things were consistent throughout the years. Mom is a worrier. One of the ways Dad took care of her was to shield her from problems with the car, the house, and with his health. Keeping these secrets was an unspoken part of his contract with her.

I see keeping secrets in a relationship as a negative, no matter how well intended. My father's secret of just how tired and ill he was resulted in my mother being blindsided by his death. As her new caregiver, I was determined to forge a different path after Dad died. This meant that Mom and I had to have a hard conversation about secrets.

In talking with her about this part of our new relationship, I explained that I was not going to shield her from the reality of what it takes to keep a 60-year-old home in good repair. She needed to know how much it costs to hire a plumber or an electrician. I also told her that if I found myself with a health issue, I would not hide it from her. While this might mean that she would worry more, perhaps even unnecessarily at times, she would not be blindsided again by a serious problem that I had kept from her.

Another part of our discussion was that I was not going to be responsible for making all the decisions about her home or her health. If there was a problem, we would talk about it and decide on how to handle it together. This became important to Mom as she took ownership of her finances. The money to keep the house in good repair is, after all, hers. It is only right that she should have control over how it is spent.

Because of my mother's mobility and eyesight, she had gotten used to a contract where Dad took responsibility for most of the tasks around the house, everything from doing laundry and paying bills to making follow-up phone calls for doctor appointments. I could not physically or mentally live up to that contract. Mom and I had to have another hard conversation about how she was asking me to take on tasks that she could be doing herself. For example, I could not take on the responsibility for making all phone calls for her. If the doctor needed a call back to confirm an appointment, I needed my mother to call rather than wait for me to do it for her. If there was a problem with the heat or the air conditioning, she could call the power company first, then let me know if something more needed to be done. Once the laundry was done, she could fold it so I could put it away. My mother delegating these small tasks to me took up a huge amount of time when I already had a home of my own.

Was it hard to make these adjustments at first? Yes, for both of us. Did we both fall back into old patterns from time to time? You bet. But here's the thing. The more Mom took on, the more empowered she felt and the more my stress level went down.

While it may be easy to identify these physical tasks in a relationship contract, it's harder to identify and articulate the emotions that are tied to that contract.

How do we support one another?

I define support as the things we do or say that makes the people in our lives feel loved, heard, and validated. How we feel supported, loved, validated, and heard often comes from childhood experiences. Watching my parents' interactions with each other, and how they supported my brother and me, shaped how I support people in my life. And it shaped my expectations for support. The truth is, my support needs are different than Mom's. Not better, not worse, just different.

Because Mom and I have forged a new contract, we have had to work through some of these differences. Our biggest hurdle has been around expectations such as the ones I've mentioned. Mom now knows she can take on additional responsibilities. Her letting go of the expectation that I could continue to make and follow up on all the phone calls clearly showed her willingness to support and care for me—in the same way that I am willing to support and care for her.

But there are emotional issues as well. This has been hard for Mom. We have developed a completely different contract than the one she had with Dad. That means that many of the small details of the way she lived her life for over 60-plus years have changed. It's hard for any of us to let go of old roles, pick up new ones, and especially come to terms with feelings of "this is not how it was supposed to be, this is not what I signed up for."

Because I changed the contract Mom had with Dad, it's important that I acknowledge how emotional these changes are for her. I often tell Mom how proud I am of her and how much I appreciate all the new things she has taken on. When I say to her, "I know how hard all these changes are," I validate her feelings. At 83 years old, after 61 years of marriage, she had to lose that person and have the life she lived change as well? It's on me to always keep in mind how different and difficult this is for her.

The truth is, my life has changed drastically as well. I've had to give up some of my own expectations. And that's hard. Before becoming Mom's caregiver, I'd started to plan a vacation to Italy and think about where I would like to retire. Now travel and retirement plans are on hold. Because I am Mom's caregiver every other weekend, there are times I would love to meet up with friends, but I can't. I would be lying if I didn't admit that I resent not having my own life anymore, and I grieve not being able to plan for the future.

What shared interests bind your relationship together?

Thinking about a relationship as a contract may seem like an unnatural point of view for you. It really isn't when you apply the lens of shared interests. Let's take the example of a couple in which one person loses weight. Suddenly, that person is no longer interested in going out to dinner or going to the movies because these activities can undermine the weight loss. If going out to dinner and getting popcorn at the movies is at the core of how you are together as a couple, that piece of the contract is now broken. Without an honest discussion about needs, wants, expectations, boundaries, and limits, the relationship can be damaged beyond repair.

My parents loved watching the Yankees. They would sit in matching recliners in the den, head phones on to hear better, and yell comments to one another about the game. It was cute and funny, if I wasn't trying to sleep. Mom has not watched a Yankee game since my father died. The companionship of watching TV and commenting on a show was a huge loss for her. It was an activity that bound their relationship together.

Despite not being a big TV person, in our unspoken caregiver contract, I keep this piece of Mom and Dad's relationship intact. In our contract, we watch cooking shows together. Am I often on my iPad while the show is on? Yes. But I'm also paying attention to her, responding to comments, and more than once I have jumped on the internet to print out a recipe.

Shared social outlets are as important as shared activities.

Mom is Italian. Growing up we had a full second kitchen in the basement just like her parents, aunts, and uncles. The oven downstairs is where the lasagna and second turkey cooked when we had 30 people for Thanksgiving dinner. Hosting gatherings, large and small, and cooking for family are how Mom loved us, and it was a huge part of our family social life.

In my childhood, cooking together had been one of the shared activities that bound Mom and my relationship together. I learned to cook by helping her prepare these holiday meals. As I moved into adulthood, we had gotten away from this shared activity.

Through the years, changes to Mom's eyesight have meant she can't cook without help. Because of that, Dad became her sous chef. Now that I've taken over his sous chef role, cooking together is a gift because it takes me back to my childhood.

So much of our mother/daughter relationship changed when I became her caregiver. Because of that, I am deliberate about keeping this piece intact in our contract. While we are cooking together, we can let go of our caregiver/caree roles. And the best part? We talk about family, reminisce about people and places, and strengthen the bonds of our relationship.

Sometimes it's the little things you change in a contract that make you feel heard and validated. For me, it was not having to make all the doctor appointments and return so many phone calls. Taking those things off my plate was such a relief. More importantly, it was one of the first times I asked Mom to let go of a piece of the contract she had with Dad. I know it wasn't easy for her, and I let her know how much I appreciated it. And she really did understand. Not long after this discussion, she once again took over emptying the dishwasher. These changes in her expectations brought me mental as well as physical relief.

And I have it relatively easy as Mom's caregiver. By that I mean I'm not married, my child is of the 4-legged, furry variety, and my work is mobile. I can't imagine how complicated and stressful your life is if you are part of the sandwich generation as someone who is married with children, working outside the home, AND responsible for helping your aging parents.

We need to recognize early on that we have these contracts in our lives and be ready to commit to the work and self-awareness it takes to change them. Changing them is not easy because we often have competing expectations. Then there is the time it takes to identify these expectations, talk about them, set boundaries, and co-create your new contract.

Don't feel guilty having those conversations and setting boundaries. Not only is this work healthy, it can save words spoken in anger. When we lash out in anger our loved one can be blindsided by it. It is not fair to get angry when someone pushes a limit you have never expressed. Boundary conversations are critical to healthy relationships.

The time to start is now. If you have started picking up groceries for your aging parents while doing your shopping, you are a caregiver. If you have started going to the doctor with your loved one to be the second set of ears, you're a caregiver. If the hair on the back of your neck stands up when you're on the phone with your mom because you're getting the feeling that she is unsafe, listen to your instincts. Your spidey sense is telling you, you are a caregiver.

Denise Brown is founder of Caregiving.com and author of "The Caregiving Years, Six Stages to a Meaningful Journey." In this book, and in her Certified Caregiving Consultant™ training, she outlines these six caregiving stages:

- ♥ Expectant: Because we all are Expectant Caregivers, we can use the time now to gather helpful information we may need later when a family member needs our help and care.
- ♥ Freshman: As we start to help, we may search for just the perfect solution. Instead of holding out for perfect, we can experiment to figure out what's good enough right now.
- ♥ Entrenched: We can feel swallowed up by our caregiving responsibilities, which impact on our day, our decisions, our energy, and our relationships. The stress may feel overwhelming, which is why we focus on receiving especially a routine that gives us a break.
- ♥ Pragmatic: We understand that surprises are now the status quo, which means we can cope with what caregiving throws at us. Because of our calm confidence, we can welcome the joys of our day.

♥ Transitioning: During our caree's end of life, we realize the power of being and understand how our presence brings comfort. We experience the transition of life and the transition in our life after caregiving. We allow both endings and beginnings.

♥ Godspeed: We understand the meaning and purpose of a life well-lived so focus on doing just that—living a good life to the best of our ability. We treasure our lessons learned.

Creating a caregiver contract can begin anywhere in these first four stages. My hope is that you begin this work in the Expectant stage, when you are just beginning to realize that caregiving is on your horizon. Life will be easier if the initial work is done before you are in the Entrenched stage—when involvement with the person you are caring for is daily, everything is new, decisions seem overwhelming, and you are second-guessing yourself.

So what is your current relationship contract? What are the unspoken expectations? What difficult conversations do you need to have in order to co-create a new, realistic, and manageable contract?

Caregiving comes to us in many ways. For me, it was a slow slide that started with Dad's congestive heart failure diagnosis. You would have thought I was prepared when I became Mom's caregiver. I was not. For others it happens very quickly. Here's a staggering statistic from a keynote speaker at the Family Resource Network 2019 national caregivers conference:

"You get nine months to plan for a baby. The typical time to plan a wedding is a year and a half. Statistically, most people get nine (yes nine!) minutes to become a caregiver. That is one phone call."

Look at the worksheets that follow. They are a great place to start when creating a caregiver contract. As I said earlier, you want to start this work early in your caregiving journey.

Exercise One
Creating Your Task List

What are we willing to do (or not do) for one another? To create this task list, you'll want to sit down with your older loved one and start a discussion about what they do day to day so you will be prepared to help them. The result should be a list of tasks, who does them, and when—from a small task like taking out the garbage to a bigger one like getting Mom to the doctor.

Not only will you get a list of tasks, but you will get a sense of expectations. Your elderly parent has done things their way for years. Asking them to additionally change the way they live their life will be challenging. There is enough change in their life with failing health, faltering mobility, and the loss of contemporaries. Going through this exercise and making the resulting list gives you an understanding of what your loved one's expectations might be for you. Creating this list allows you to be thinking about what you are willing and able to take on. It's a great list to share with siblings and others in your support network.

Don't expect a complete list in one setting; keep adding to it over time. It will change over time as well. When you work together to put tasks down on paper, you open the door to new solutions. More importantly, you start to become a team.

Start the discussion in a nonthreatening way.

♥ "Mom, can you help me to understand when you need to put your garbage or recycling out, just in case I ever need to help you with this task?"

♥ "Dad, what grocery store do you use, and do you like to go on a particular day?" "Can we make a list together so that I know what brand of cereal is your favorite?"

♥ "Dad, where is the lawn mower, and how often do you like to mow the lawn? I know your grandchild would like to help.

Maybe he/she could cut the grass once in a while when you don't feel like doing it."

This discussion is not about telling them they shouldn't be mowing the lawn. It is about:
♥ Understanding how they live their daily lives
♥ Knowing likes and dislikes so you or someone else can smoothly take over a task
♥ Keeping the control with them

Once you know what the task is, when it needs to be done, and who currently does it, you can open the next level of discussion:
♥ Is it something you can do as the caregiver or can someone else in the family do it?
♥ Do you need to hire someone to do it?

I can't keep up my home and Mom's, especially through the summer when the lawn needs to be cut weekly. My brother who lives 12 hours away pays for a service to cut Mom's lawn. He can't give me physical help in caregiving, but he contributes in meaningful ways to Mom's care.

Once you know the what, when, who, and how, you can open the next level of discussion:
♥ Does this task still need to be done this way? If Mom or Dad goes grocery shops on Tuesday, senior citizens discount day, but you can't shop that day, what would a new solution look like? Can you set up a shop at home system for them and pick it up on Tuesday?

Sample Task List
This is a task list I made for Mom and me.

Task	Who	When	Solution?
Garbage	Dad	Tuesday night after 5:00	Pay young adult in the neighborhood
Recycling	Dad	Every 2 weeks put out on Sunday for pickup	Pay young adult in the neighborhood
Pick up prescriptions	Mom and Dad	Every 30 days	Go to a mail subscription service and ask the doctor for a 90-day scripts
Medication management	Dad	Weekly	Me: Set up a month at a time
Insulin shots	Dad	Daily	Me: Set up 2 weeks at a time
Grocery shopping	Dad	Weekly	Set up shop from home account and pick up every 2 weeks
Clean house	Dad	Bi-Monthly	Hire service
Pay bills	Dad	Weekly	Hire a money manager
Banking reconciliation	Dad	Monthly	Me: monthly
Submit to insurance	Dad	Monthly	Hire a money manager
Schedule maintenance work for AC/generator	Dad	Quarterly	Me: Put on automatic reminder
Renew insurances	Dad	Yearly	Me: Set up calendar reminders

Exercise Two
Creating Your Support Network Contact List

I live almost an hour away from my mother. When my dad died, I didn't know who he used for a plumber, electrician, or any of the other support systems he had in place. I spent hours one weekend going through his phone book, computer, and hard copy files to get this list. Thankfully, he did leave me with all the contact information for bank accounts, insurance policies, and investments, including URLs, sign-on IDs, and passwords. But if a pipe burst, who did he trust to call?

This contact list is the beginning of your support network. The benefits of having this list is staggering, especially if you don't live close. How I approached our contact list is based on the work of Dr. Glenna Crook, author of "The Networksage: Realize Your Network Superpower." In this book, Dr. Crooks describes networks, and challenges you to think about yours with three questions:

♥ Who are the people in your life?
♥ What is it you want and need that they can provide?
♥ If the support they provide doesn't serve you well, how should you make changes to be sure you can accomplish your objectives?

In creating a list of those who played a role in Mom's life, I had the beginning of our support network. Then, in thinking about what *Mom and I* needed and wanted, holes in our support network became apparent. For example, when we talked about service providers, it was clear our plumber was good, but we needed a new electrician. Creating a support network contact list, just like the task list, is a team effort and is not about taking away control. Again, don't expect it to be complete in one sitting.

Start the discussion in a nonthreatening way.
♥ "Dad, if you and Mom were out of the house or away, and Don next door called to tell me there was water coming out the front door, who is your plumber so I could call them?"
♥ "Mom, if your internet stopped working, who is your provider? Do you have the phone number handy?"
♥ "Can we make a list of important service providers you use that I can take home with me? Just in case for some reason I needed to call and schedule something for you."

Sample Service Provider List

Here is a sample list. You can fill this out and add other providers that you need.

Account Type	Provider	Account Number	Phone Number	Website	Password
Gas					
Electric					
Internet					
Telephone (house)					
Mobile phone					
Plumber					
Electrician					
Landscaper					
Handyman					
Insurance agent					
Investment advisor					
Bank checking					
Bank savings					
401 K					
Pension					
Social Security					
Primary doctor					
Specialists					
Prescriptions					
Veterinarian					

Chapter 2
Life Changes for Everyone

My parents met at a Sweet Sixteen party. Each had come with a date, but when spin the bottle started, my mother called my father's number, over and over again. When Dad told this story, he always ended it by mimicking throwing out a fishing line and reeling in the catch. Then he would smile.

I love these family stories. In hearing them and observing my parents' relationship contract, I figured out early on that my mother chose a man who was the direct opposite of her father. That realization gave me a lot of insight into my mother and has helped as we co-create our caregiving contract and navigate the changes in our mother/daughter relationship.

In Chapter One of this book we started to explore what happens when a relationship contract is broken or needs adjustment. It may happen through a death, as it did in my family. It can occur because of a healthcare crisis. A new living situation may be the reason a relationship contract needs adjusting. In this chapter we are going to dig deeper and explore why it is important to keep the following ideas in mind while co-creating a caregiver contract.

♥ Please don't "parent your parent."

♥ The words you use and the way you present change matters.

♥ The changes you are asking your elderly parent to make are emotional, for you and for them.

♥ The important term to remember is "co-create." You and your parent are going to create something together that works for both of you.

Please don't "parent your parent"

Throughout our caregiving years, we can fall into the trap of trying to parent our parents. In the early years, safety is typically the biggest concern. You may find yourself saying things such as "you need to move into assisted living where you'll be safe," or "you need to stop driving," or a hundred other admonitions that take away their independence. The words "you must," "you need to," "you should," or their countless other variations are not a particularly productive way to bring about change in a person who has been doing things a certain way since before you were born. Yes, your parent did change your diapers and made sure you wore a coat when it was cold and told you what was best in your life when you were a child. Using the language of a parent to a child makes co-creating a caregiver contract almost impossible.

I first realized the importance of the language we use, and how important it is to recognize and honor our loved one's need to keep control of their life, after reading the book *How to Say It® to Seniors: Closing the Communication Gap with Our Elders* by David Solie, M.S., P. A.

Finding this book early on in my caregiving was a gift. In it, Mr. Solie discusses some of the frustrating behaviors of aging loved ones. They often repeat stories. They seem to fret over unimportant details, hindering our ability to resolve issues. In the book, he shares what he sees as the two critical needs of our seniors:

♥ "To maintain control is a primary driver for the elderly, because each day, they feel losses—of strength, health, peers, and authority that are staggering."

This need to maintain control is where the language we use as caregivers matters. Conversations that take away control, such as "you need to move because your bedroom and bathroom are upstairs," will more than likely have your senior digging in their heels. When you acknowledge their desire and offer alternatives, you often have a place to start negotiations.

And:

♥ "The developmental work of our elderly is to look 'backward, not forward' to reflect on what their lives have meant to themselves, their loved ones, and the world at large."

When we listen to stories of our loved one's life, when we ask them to tell their stories so others can hear them, we are helping them to process their life, their legacy. As David Solie points out in his book, this is important work, and it's the last developmental work our loved one will do. Lately, as Mom and I cook together, she has been telling me stories from her childhood. Some I have heard before, and some I have not. But I am struck by how often she ends a story with a comment like "Oh well, they did the best they could." This is legacy processing, coming to a new insight about people or events in your life.

The other trap we can fall into occurs as your loved one's health declines. It is often easier to just "do" for them. "Here, Mom, sit down so I can tie your shoes." "Dad, stand there a minute while I take your coat off." But the "doing" can take away choice and independence. In the long run, doing for your parent the things he or she can still do can impact their future ability to perform these tasks for themselves.

I get it. It takes longer for Dad to sit down, slowly take off his coat, slowly get back up, hang it—slowly—in the closet, and sit back down. Yes, it's frustrating while you wait. You have so much on your caregiver to-do list, never mind what you need to get done for yourself and your family waiting at home. Why not just get it done quickly and easily? But in taking over, you are taking away what independence your parent has left, and that is just one more loss in a sea of losses.

A very wise friend of mine, Rachel Hiles, is her grandmother's caregiver. She has experience working with adults living with disabilities and blogs about her caregiving adventures on her website, www.TakingCareofGrandma.com. Rachel is 100% on target when she says, "Caregiving is not the same as parenting. Our elders' lifetime of experience is unique, forged over lifelong habits and preferences. As caregivers, it is our responsibility to honor these."

I realized this early on as my father's caregiver. Dad's last year of life was very difficult. I knew how exhausted he was when he agreed to let my brother and I pay to have Certified Home Health Aides (CHHAs) come in six hours a week for laundry and light housekeeping. Another clue was when he let me take over the grocery shopping. I really understood when he would rest while I drove him to the doctor. The truth is, Dad needed help with these tasks long before he accepted it. But as an adult with full mental capacity, I could not force him. I had to respect his decisions. I suspect part of his waiting so long to accept help was based on not wanting my mother to know how truly sick he was feeling.

And boy did I have to deal with emotions after we lost him. Would he have lived longer if he'd accepted help earlier? Should I have pushed harder? If I did would we still have him in our lives? I don't know, but I must believe, knowing my dad as I did, that allowing him to live and die on his own terms was one of the last gifts I could give him.

These last years as Mom's caregiver, as well as in my work as a Certified Caregiving Consultant™, have continued to show me how we must honor our loved one's experiences and desires. It is in trying to find the middle ground, where our desires and needs intersect with our loved one's desires and needs, that a caregiving contract will help.

Meeting in the middle takes work. The biggest hurdle we have as our elderly parents' caregiver is to come to terms with this truth. *If your loved one has the mental capacity, he or she has the right to make the wrong decision.* You can only try to keep them safe in that decision. This is HARD. But recognizing it is essential to a new relationship caregiver contract.

Too often our concern for health and safety becomes the single biggest factor in caregiving for our parents. We discount their need to direct their own life, which is something everyone needs at each stage in their life. It is our job as caregivers to find a way to balance our desire for Mom or Dad to be healthy and safe with our parents' desire for independence and autonomy. Co-creating your caregiver contract will help you find that balance.

What are we willing to do (or not do) for one another?

So far, we have been talking about our willingness to perform tasks that don't get into the nitty-gritty of caregiving. By that I mean we haven't delved into helping with deeply personal tasks such as dressing, bathing, or even more intimate medical needs such as changing a colostomy bag. The reality of our caregiving years is that we start helping with personal tasks that have far less emotion around them: picking up groceries or laying out clothes for the next day. But at some point, your parents will need help with tasks that can make everyone feel very uncomfortable and touch on personal boundaries.

Caregiving can be a slippery slope. The slide may be slow and insidious, or one event—like a fall—can plunge you into it full time. Either way, you may find yourself helping in ways that make your loved one feel vulnerable, while you are faced with tasks that you may not be fully prepared to take on.

Most parents want to stay at home, or "age-in-place." The truth is, it is usually little things like not being able to shower or use a can opener that become the reason why someone cannot stay at home.

There are two standards used by the healthcare industry—Activities of Daily Living and Instrumental Activities of Daily Living—that define what it takes to live independently at home. Once you know these standards, you can gauge for yourself how much help your parent needs.

Activities of Daily Living (ADLs)

ADLs are the normal daily activities that a person does for themselves throughout the day.

- ♥ Can the person go to the bathroom, dress, and brush their teeth without help?
- ♥ Can the person get in and out of the bath?
- ♥ Does the person walk with a steady gate?
- ♥ Can the person go upstairs without help?
- ♥ Can the person feed themselves?
- ♥ Can the person dress without help?

Instrumental Activities of Daily Living (IADLs)

IADLs are the activities and tasks that are needed to live independently at home.

- ♥ Is your loved one struggling to prepare meals, do laundry, keep up with housekeeping?
- ♥ Is your loved one having trouble using the telephone, paying bills, or taking medications?
- ♥ Is your loved one still able get to doctor's appointments, go grocery shopping, or do the banking?

Please don't bury your head in the sand. Assess your parents ADLs and IADLs quietly but constantly.

Knowledge is power. It allows you to be proactive because you recognize what help is or will be needed. It gives you time to think through your expectations and boundaries as a caregiver. And you can plan better for those hard conversations.

While they are still somewhat independent, be thinking about what you can do as their caregiver, both physically and emotionally. I'm not good with blood and gore. As a child, I dreamed about being a nurse, then realized that feeling faint at the sight of blood was not going to get me far in that profession. If there comes a time when Mom needs help with wound care, I fully expect we will hire someone to help.

Once you have some idea of what is coming, or even if you are thrown into caregiving quickly, the when and how of even the most personal of tasks can be negotiated. Let's take bathing as an example. Many seniors stop bathing daily when it becomes too much of an effort. Showering every couple of days is not a health risk. Not showering at all and relying only on a "bird bath," when you wash up hurriedly in a sink, IS a health risk.

The first step is getting the OK to help with such a personal task. Some seniors are motivated by health concerns. You can try to open the discussion by citing studies from the medical community on the health risks of not showering. Another way would be to leave an article on the subject laying around the house.

Some seniors feel strongly about privacy, but they don't realize there are resources that can keep them safe in the bathroom requiring less supervision. For example, transfer chairs make getting in and out of a tub or shower safer. In addition, grab bars can be installed easily, inexpensively, and make sense in many rooms in addition to the bathroom. Handrails in a hallway can negate the need for a walker.

You know your loved one best. Use that knowledge to determine the right approach, and don't be surprised if you need to try more than one approach. Don't expect it to be a one and done conversation.

Whatever you do, I beg of you, don't start the conversation with "You need to…" or make it about their choices. These openings will shut down the conversation before it even begins. "You need to stop driving. Your reflexes have really slowed down, and continuing to drive is dangerous." "Why are you standing on that step stool? Don't you know you can fall?"

It is better to begin these discussions using this technique: a nonthreatening comment or question, an expression of concern, and a suggestion or open-ended question.

"Mom, I've noticed several things in your refrigerator have expired. I'm worried that you're not getting enough fresh produce and protein in your diet. When I cook for the week on Sunday, I'd like to drop off some fresh food that you can easily reheat. Would do you think?"

Now what?

Your parent has agreed he or she needs help bathing and is willing to have you help. How do you fit this new task into your schedule?

If your senior is used to showering in the morning but you must be at work too early, then it is time to negotiate a change to that schedule.

♥ Are they willing to bathe at night?
♥ Can you agree to one day on the weekend and one morning during the week that works with your schedule?
♥ Can you share this task with a sibling whose schedule is more flexible, or have them take it over completely?

And by negotiate I do mean listening to how your loved one is used to living his or her life and discussing how you can meet in the middle to accommodate your schedule along with their need for help.

I can almost hear you sigh and say, "I wish I could get my mom to let me help with bathing." Remember what I said earlier? If your loved one has mental capacity, they have the right to make the wrong decision. You can only try to keep them safe in that decision. This is why caregiving is so hard. This is why it is so important for each of us to constantly monitor ADLs and IADLs and think about potential solutions so that we can move quickly if needed.

Now I can almost hear you say, "But if Mom does fall and need help, I will be the one helping." True. Since knowledge is power, having some idea of what might be needed and what your loved one can afford allows you to have a conversation that is based on your boundaries without trying to change theirs. Honestly stating, "Mom, if you fall and break you hip, I will not be able to leave work and take care of you. Once you are out of the hospital and rehabilitation, would you rather come back home with an aide to help you or move into assisted living? Either way, we need to figure out finances so we are prepared."

Initially, helping Mom with more personal tasks was embarrassing for both of us, especially as I found myself doing things for her—like helping her get ready to bathe—that she did for me as a child. But making a joke about it and then having a practical discussion got us through this new stage in our caregiving. It's important to have the discussion so that you know what your loved one needs, where personal boundaries are (yours and theirs), and how you can best assist in a way that is comfortable for everyone.

One word of caution: If your loved one does agree to let you help with more personal tasks, don't parent them. These are many of the same tasks we perform for our children, and it is too easy to fall into that "parenting" mode. Your senior already feels vulnerable and emotional about needing your help. They don't need to feel condescended to, even if that is NOT your intent.

I'd like you to consider something else: Maybe bathing is not the place to start. Find something that is less personal, makes them feel less vulnerable such as grocery shopping, and then negotiate that task first. It gives everyone a chance to learn the rules of engagement on a less threatening topic while co-creating a caregiver contract.

Here is another truth. As caregivers we often feel compelled to do it all. But you can't. There are many caring people in the field of home care that can take over those personal care routines you or your parent find embarrassing. Yes, this type of help is currently private pay, but having a professional in twice a week to help with showering can be money well spent.

How do we support one another?

The words you use and the way you present change matters.

Let's face it, starting a discussion about helping someone to bathe or dress is difficult. Try keeping it lighthearted if possible, and then have the practical discussion. "Hey Mom, we're at that stage in life where I get to help you like you helped me. And if my daughter thinks she's getting away with not doing the same for me, boy is she in for a surprise! How can I help make your bathing routine easier?" Humor really does help.

When it comes to deeply personal tasks, the mistake we can make is to have them fall into the unspoken part of our contract. It is because there is so much emotion around personal boundaries that we should address these tasks with loving and supportive words. Otherwise, an emotion like embarrassment can come out in harsh words spoken hastily while helping with the personal task. Start a discussion ahead of time. Use a nonthreatening comment, express concern, and ask a question.

Here are some examples:

"I'm concerned that it's getting harder for you to get up and down the stairs as much as you used to. I know you want to stay here. But it worries me that the only bathroom is upstairs. What do we need to do in this house for you to be able to live comfortably?"

"I worry about you being alone at home. Do you feel safe getting in and out of the shower? There are inexpensive things we can do to keep you safe. For example, they make pretty grab bars these days; they don't look so 'hospital like.'"

Supportive conversations followed up by actions you agree to are the key elements to co-creating a caregiver contract. Perhaps the most comfortable way to assist your loved one in bathing is to lay everything out, turn on the water, help them into the shower, and leave them in peace. This routine keeps them safe and honors their need for some privacy. But you only get to this type of workable arrangement through conversation.

Along with having multiple conversations on any one routine, expect to modify the changed routine more than once. Talking about how to help a person get ready and into the shower, and then doing it are two different things. Your loved one's abilities will decline over time, which can require another conversation. My hope is that all changes quickly become a new normal.

When you are tired, stressed, or on a time constraint, supporting your senior, not parenting them, is the hardest part of caregiving. Listen to yourself. If you hear that parental tone in your voice, stop, take a breath, and start over. The words you use and your tone of voice matters so choose them carefully.

What social outlets and tasks bind your relationship together?

The changes we ask our elderly parent to make are emotional—both for you and for them.

As caregivers we must acknowledge and consider how much is changing for our elderly parents. While they are losing the people who share their history, they are also losing health and mobility, all of which leads to a loss of independence and perhaps the biggest loss—a way of life they have always known. In addition, as health declines so does your senior's ability to deal with changes in routine or a household problem. What used to be no big deal is now overwhelming.

Imagine how you would feel if asked these questions: "Do you need me to help you get dressed?" "Are you OK going to the bathroom?" After all, your parent has been performing these tasks on their own since long before you were born. Sometimes helping is a natural outgrowth of coming home from the hospital or rehabilitation so these questions may not occur. But the emotions, oh the emotions, are there no matter how we begin to help with caregiver tasks.

Here's the thing: The more personal the caregiving task, the more it can strengthen your relationship. Or drive a wedge in it. Energy is required to approach caregiving in a way that gets past all the emotional baggage and binds the relationship closer. The truth is, caregiving has a way of bringing back past hurts, raw emotions, and grief—for you, and your loved one.

Try not to get frustrated with what may seem like a negative attitude. It really is physically exhausting to live in an old body. They are tired, and it can make them scared and unable to cope like they used to.

I realized the truth of this one morning, not long after Dad's release from the hospital, while we were having breakfast together. Suddenly, he looked up in panic and almost in tears. He couldn't remember if he had reapplied for the grant that paid for his macular degeneration shots. Without that grant, he could not afford them. Seeing my father, my rock, scared, overwhelmed, and so close to tears broke my heart.

All of which leads us to grief. Grief is one of the most unrecognized emotions for seniors and their caregivers. While our seniors are grieving the loss of friends and family, as well as the loss of mobility and independence, we as caregivers are grieving the loss of our parents. The foundation of our world is changing, and it will never be the same. We mourn the loss of our parent/child relationship. And we mourn the loss of our own freedom and independence. It's a lot to take on.

So how do you get past the emotions? It takes work and practice. When I am feeling unheard, unappreciated, or stressed, I get angry, and my inner eight-year-old comes roaring out. I must work hard to first recognize it, then rein it in.

It's not easy, but it is the first step. By the same token, when Mom is feeling unheard, unappreciated, and like a burden to me, my mother reacts to me like I am her father. It is never my intent to make her feel like this, but it happens. And it usually happens when my inner eight-year-old reigns.

The second step is to find ways to be together that take you out of the caregiver/caree roles. One way to do that is to make a list of noncaregiving tasks that can bind the relationship together. These are the tasks that your senior loves to do and would enjoy having company doing them. Think about:

- ♥ Cooking together
- ♥ Playing cards or a board game
- ♥ Going out to dinner or hosting dinner at their house
- ♥ Going to church or a movie
- ♥ Going for a ride in the country

One of the benefits of this list, especially if you live far away, is that you can ask, "Did you play bridge last night?" If the answer is no several weeks in a row, that is a red flag that something is going on.

You may have some work to do to prepare your loved one to go to church or host a dinner. But the reward is their renewed joy in daily living so it is well worth it. You may even learn something new about your loved one as you create this list together. Creating ways to spend time together and then making the time gives you both a break from the roles of caregiver and caree.

Co-creating a caregiver contract

As caregivers, we get into trouble when we don't recognize the parent/child relationship has changed. We get into trouble when we continue the same patterns of behavior or try to continue to give care in a way that is unsustainable. We get into trouble when we don't renegotiate our caregiver contract.

I'm not going to lie. Co-creating this is hard work. The process will bring up difficult emotions.

♥ Don't expect it to go smoothly in the beginning; change is not easy for our seniors or for us.

♥ Co-creating a caregiver contract requires honest, supportive conversation—a skill that many of us need to practice.

♥ Co-creating a contract is not a one and done activity. It will need to change as circumstances change, both yours and your parents.

♥ Co-creating a contract means getting beyond your inner eight-your-old and past hurts.

I can honestly say that in co-creating a caregiver contract with my mother, our relationship is better than when I was a child. That's something that continually surprises me and for which I am very grateful.

In this chapter I introduced some of the skills, language, and conflicting desires that must be addressed to co-create a successful caregiver contract. A successful caregiver contract is one that works for you as the primary caregiver, and for your parent as the care recipient. In the following chapters we will delve deeper into these topics, but these three concepts hold true for every aspect of negotiating.

♥ Don't "parent your parent."

♥ Language matters.

♥ Making these changes is emotional for everyone.

In the examples and worksheet that follow, you will find suggestions for supportive conversation starters and suggestions for activities that take you out of the caregiver/caree role. Our goal is always to get to where your loved one welcomes help instead of resenting it.

Exercise Three
Activities of Daily Living (ADLs) and Instrumental Activities of Daily Living (IADLs) Checklist*

Use this worksheet to determine which ADLs and IADLs your loved one requires assistance on and how much assistance is needed. You can use a score of 1 to 3 to indicate when an ADL moves up the "Some Assistance Needed" scale but "Complete Assistance Needed" does not apply.

There is no right or wrong for the scale of 1 to 3 so use your best judgment. Scoring this way allows small changes to be caught early and supports your concerns with other family members about ongoing deterioration of ADLs and IADLs. Update frequently.

Example: Changes to bathing scoring over time
1. Bathroom needs to be prepped for a shower—towels laid out; water turned on
2. Needs help getting into the walk-in shower
3. Needs help washing hair

ADLs / IADLs	Requires No Assistance	Some Assistance Needed	Complete Assistance Needed	Notes
Bathing				
Dressing				
Grooming				
Oral care				
Toileting				
Transferring				
Walking				
Climbing stairs				
Eating				
Shopping				
Cooking				
Managing medications				
Uses the phone				
Housework				
Laundry				
Driving				
Managing finances				
Totals				

* Developed by PBS.org and AARP. Adapted: Advocate for Mom and Dad, LLC

Exercise Four
Conversation Starters

Recognize that, as their child, it requires a delicate balance to offer help in a way that does not demean your parent or make them feel like your child.

1. Ask the question: "What do you want me to do?" It is a great way to start the conversation. It gives them control and the opportunity to say "yes" to help without taking away independence because they are driving the solution.

2. At other times, offer several suggestions for them to choose from and then decide as a family on the best course of action. This is the start to a relationship based on teamwork.

3. If researching the answer to a problem is beyond your parents' current coping mechanisms, with permission, do the research for them. It is important to concentrate on alternatives that honor that this is still their house and life.

4. When asked, give them your honest opinion.

5. Given your parents' physical limitations, be careful not to say "let me do it," or take something away and do it for them. I realized this when I had to stop myself from grabbing the ketchup bottle out of my mother's hands to put some on her dish. Instead, say "Can I help you?" And then abide by their answer. I know sometimes you wind up cleaning up what they did for themselves and it's frustrating. But we are back to not parenting our parents.

Exercise Five
Questions That Open the Door to Change

Here are some questions to ask that can help you get to a workable caregiver contract for everyone:

1. What outside help can we look for and say "yes" to that will make the things we need to get done around the house more manageable?
    ♥ "I can't keep up with the outside of my house and yours. Is there someone you trust that we can hire to cut the lawn? If not, I have some suggestions."

2. What rituals throughout the day can we change, modify, or do away with today?

♥ "Mom, I know you can't put away the clothes, but it would be helpful if you can fold them while you're sitting down and then I can put them away."

Bottom line: When it comes to living and household decisions, being your parents' partner, not acting like their parent, works. They still feel in control of their lives, which is important to them and should be important to you as well.

Exercise Six
Social Outlets Help Isolation and Loneliness

Not long ago Mom and I were in the kitchen getting ready for the next day when friends were coming over to dinner. In that familiar rhythm of cooking together, she suddenly asked me what famous person I would like to have dinner with. What followed was a lovely conversation in which we both shared our list of politicians, authors, and TV personalities. It turns out we share a desire to sit down to dinner and have a conversation with many of the same people. From there she related a story I had never heard before from her childhood. She reminisced about parties hosted by the town in which everyone would congregate in the town square to mingle and dance. It is in these times that I can see and hear my mother processing her legacy.

There are so many losses in your senior's life that finding things to do together (which for my mom and me is cooking) will ease the more difficult tasks you undertake as the caregiver. As you build this list together, take the opportunity to learn more about your loved one's legacy.

♥ Did they ever sing in a choir in the community or in their faith community?
♥ Who taught them to play bridge?
♥ What is their favorite card game to play and why?
♥ What is their favorite movie, TV show and why?
♥ What is their signature dish to cook?
♥ What was their best golf handicap?
♥ What position did they play on their high school football or basketball team?

Recognize that the person involved in these social outlets doesn't always have to be you.

♥ Can you ask someone from church to pick up your loved one?

♥ Can a niece or grandson stop by for a movie or to play cards?

Social Outlets Sample List

Here is a sample list of activities your loved one would like to continue.

I would like to:	What is required for this activity?	Who can help us fulfill this wish list?
Go to church	Requires a ride at 9:30 on Sunday	Church member or friend
Play cards	Need cards with big numbers; favorite game is Aggravation	Anyone willing! Mom can teach them the game. She likes to bet pennies; be prepared!
Cook	Anyone able to stand at the stove to stir, lift heavy pots, put things into the oven. Likes to bake banana bread to give away	Anyone willing! Mom knows the recipe. Someone will need to make sure everything is in the house ahead of time
Watch football or baseball together	Any Sunday they play	Someone who understands the game
Play golf	Any day possible	Someone who can drive the cart
Book club	Third Wednesday of the month	Someone who loves to read and can drive
Walking/Exercise	As often as possible	Anyone who doesn't mind a slower pace and conversation
Shopping for fun	Any availability	Someone who drives/ can manage a rollator in and out of the car
Going out to dinner	Any availability	Someone who drives/ can manage a rollator in and out of the car

Chapter 3
An Emotional Journey

Years ago, the comedian George Carlin did a routine based on "the seven words you can't say on TV." At the time it was shocking; some people found it offensive, others laughed and agreed with him. The emotions you feel as a caregiver can have the same effect on people in your life. Some are shocked that you feel that way, others are offended that you are expressing harsh emotions, and others will shake their head, laugh, and agree with you. This last group of folks are my caregiver peeps. My hope is that you will find yours.

Here is my list of the seven emotions and feelings I still find hard to admit to having as a caregiver—even after five years on this journey:

Fear
Overwhelmed
Guilt
Anger
Resentment
Frustration
Grief

I'm here to assure you that all your emotions are perfectly normal. Yours may be different than mine. You may call it panic instead of fear. But as a caregiver you will feel a host of emotions, often when you least expect it. You may think "I'm done with feeling guilty." Then something unexpected occurs, and you are right back to feeling that guilt except now you're angry because you feel guilty again!

I've found the best thing I can do is name and own my emotions and feelings. In doing so, I can get to the flip side of them:

Confidence

Forgiveness

Clarity

Love

Contentment

Gratification

Happiness

In Chapter Two we recognize that the changes we ask of our elderly parent are steeped in emotion, both for you and for them. In the whirlwind of caregiving it can be hard to recognize our emotions, which makes it hard to get to the other side. If you "don't name and claim them, you can't change them." And I firmly believe only you can affect your emotions. You can't change your parents, but you can find new ways to interact and to break old patterns by exploring what is happening in your relationship and what role you play in these dynamics.

Negotiating a caregiver contract is a process. We need to be careful about giving up too quickly. It's easy to say, "Mom will never change." "It's happened before, I know it will happen again." To step out of our negative thoughts, we need to listen; hear their frustration and pain. Only then can we understand their point of view, help them understand our point of view, respond with love, and co-create a caregiver contract.

Let me give you a real-world example of this process of co-creating a caregiver contract through listening, putting aside your emotions, and having a conversation can work.

Not long after Dad died, I received an invitation to a family party via text message. I happened to be with Mom and, with real pleasure, read the text message to her. Mom got quiet and then said, "I feel invisible." When I asked her what she meant, she said, "All the invitations are coming to you. People use texts and all that stuff, and I can't use it. I feel like I died. I feel invisible."

Because of Mom's eyesight, she can't participate in emailing, texting, or Facebook. And in this age when social media is the preferred means of communication, invitations were sent to me. Mom loves to catch up with family and friends when she phones to RSVP. It was part of her role as family "social secretary," a role she loved. Invitations sent to me, not her, were just one more loss brought about by Dad's death.

As her daughter and advocate, I knew I had to do something. I called my cousin and let her know that Mom was feeling invisible and why. I let other family members know as well and asked them to call her with invitations. When an invitation means I need to be available to take Mom, people still check with me first. But they call and invite her, and these calls turn into a conversation that brightens her day.

Fast forward two years to a phone call from that same cousin. They were having an impromptu birthday dinner for her twins at a restaurant right by Mom's house. Mom and I were invited. Could we make it?

Have you ever had the experience of having your brain split in two—when you're thinking along two different paths at the same time? One half of my brain immediately goes into caregiver mode: "OK, I can cancel plans with my friends. I can rearrange my day and, if I leave by 4:30, can get to Mom's by 5:30, load the wheelchair in the car, and make it to the restaurant by 6 o'clock." The other half of my brain went into full resentment mode: "I can't believe I have to rearrange my schedule again! This is so frustrating; I'm exhausted just thinking about how to make it work."

Then I really listened and heard what my cousin was saying. And my brain splits again. "Did she just offer to pick up Mom and get her to the restaurant?" My mother who needs her "go-cart" and a wheelchair to leave the house? My mother who has never gone through this process with anyone but my dad or I because she trusts no one else?

This was one of those God-given moments when opportunity intersects with new habits. This gathering was with her family, of which she is the matriarch. Her family that she loves and that love her, in all her glory. This particular set of cousins is who we spend most of our holidays with, so I've learned to step back and have them help Mom out of my car and into their home. And this celebration was going to be a big, extended family celebration. She would not want to miss it.

So, wait for it, I say, "I'm sorry. As much as I would love to join you, I can't. But I really want Mom to go. In fact, Mom needs to know that she can trust someone other than me to help her into the car. Do me a favor. Call her, invite her, and I will talk to her as well."

"Just so you know, we have a way of getting out of the house and into the car that makes Mom feel safe. Let me tell you about it. Put the dogs out back first so their barking doesn't disturb her concentration. It takes a lot of effort for her to get to the car. Make sure she has her sunglasses on; they help cut down on glare. She uses her go-cart to walk to the front door, then she uses her cane to get down the one step. As soon as she picks up her cane, move the cart out of the way. She will hold onto the cane and grab bar at the door to come down the step, then she holds onto the ramp handrails. Move the cart and cane down to the bottom of the ramp and place it on the sidewalk at the end of the ramp. Mom uses the handrails as she walks down so she won't need her cane. Then she will use the go-cart to walk to the car. It's best if you guide the cart, but don't pull it; she will push it at the pace she needs. Once you get to the car, she will grab the door handle and steady herself on the car. The door is too heavy for her to open completely so you will need to slowly open it all the way for her. Once she sits in the car, she needs help getting her left foot in, then the rest she can do herself. Are you sure you're up for this?" My cousin assured me that she was and that Mom could tell her if she was going too fast or needed her to do something differently.

Then I called Mom and told her about the invitation. I let her know that I could come if I rearranged my day and cancelled dinner plans. I let her know that Sue had offered to pick her up and bring her to the restaurant. She was hesitant; I let her express her fears and validated that I understood why she was reluctant and nervous. I reassured her that Sue had the same car as I do so she would be familiar with it. I reminded her that she trusts Sue to help her into her house with the go-cart and wheelchair. And I told her I thought it was important that she learn that she could get out of the house with someone other than me. What if I was out of town or sick? But the final decision was up to her. She could go with Sue, I could rearrange my schedule, or she could decline the invitation. Once she decided to go, I sent a text to my cousin and asked her to finalize the plans. Then I stepped back. I didn't try to manage the process.

And it worked. My cousin helped her out of the house, into the car, brought her into the restaurant in her wheelchair, and then reversed the process. And me? I got a picture of the family at the restaurant while I was out to dinner with my friends.

I want to share this story to illustrate how often honest conversations, setting expectations, dealing with emotions, and SAYING "YES" TO HELP come into play in our caregiving journey. Because I listened when my mother said she felt isolated, I am now deliberate in finding opportunities to get out of the house. We might go for a drive or she may accompany me while I run errands. We take advantage of as many social invitations as possible. Sometimes we visit, and sometimes we host. This is part of my caregiving contract with her. Because I know how important seeing family is to Mom, I knew that she would not want to miss the birthday celebration. Because we have been having honest conversations, I knew I could tell her how important it was to me that she learn that she could leave the house with someone other than me. And because of honest conversations, she knows how important it is to my mental and physical health that I spend time with my friends, my support system.

Name them, claim them, then change them

When I started on this caregiving journey, panic was my first emotion. I would lay in bed at night and think: Where do I start? How am I going to be Mom's caregiver when my job required me to be out of state Monday through Thursday? Where could I find someone we trusted to be with her when I was not? Would she even accept a stranger in her home? How was I going to be able to keep up my home and hers?

Panic was soon joined by feeling overwhelmed. There were so many decisions to make and so many choices to sift through before a decision could be made. Who could guide me to the best choice for Mom? How can I be sure that the choice I made would be the right one—physically, emotionally, and financially—for Mom?

I remember one weekend after Dad died. I spent 12 hours going over three years of bank and credit card statements. Dad had left me all the financial information including income, investments, phone numbers, and passwords. But I had no idea of where their money went and what bills needed to be paid when. And I was worried about how we could afford the help we needed so where could I cut the budget and save money? That process, those hours I spent looking over expenses, was necessary but completely overwhelming. It just added to the stress of having to contact institutions and companies to let them know Dad was dead, figure out what needed to be cancelled, and what needed to be put in Mom's name.

Five years in, I wish I could tell you that fear and feeling overwhelmed have completely disappeared. I'd be lying if I told you that. Panic, which completely immobilized me initially, has given way to the more productive emotion of fear. I say productive because I've learned that fear gives me room to think, talk to people, weigh options, and move onto a decision with some level of confidence. Do I still get overwhelmed? Absolutely. But I'm not in this alone. Mom and I are a team, and we talk about what needs to happen and about our options. Talking our options through comforts me and gives clarity to my thoughts. Forging our team would have been impossible if we hadn't renegotiated our contract.

Am I completely confident in every decision Mom and I make? No, but I'm confident that the decision we make today is the right one for today. After five years as a caregiver, I know circumstances will change. I know we will have to rethink and change what we are doing. That's OK because I am confident that with the information we have at the time, we will make the best decision we can. The gift in these last five years is that I've learned to give up control and to forgive myself if a decision is not perfect.

Guilt

Then there is guilt, which is always waiting to rear its ugly head. There is that little niggle in your brain: Am I doing enough? Am I doing the right thing? How can I split myself and do a better job at work, at home, and with Mom? The good news is, once you realize you are making the right decision for today, you can learn to let go of this type of guilt and forgive yourself for decisions that didn't work out the way you planned.

Now Mom guilt, that's a little harder. When I'm tired and stressed I am not the nicest person, and I will take it out on Mom. And I feel guilty for doing it. I've discovered that apologizing to Mom for my words or attitude results in forgiveness. Forgiveness from her, in turn, allows me to forgive myself.

I think guilt is the one emotion that can get caregivers into deep trouble. In the heat of the moment, we can be guilted into a promise that is impossible to keep. For example, I am infuriated every time I see a commercial by a Home Care Agency. You know the one: "You're keeping Mom at home because you promised Dad you would."

This marketing message feeds into the subliminal idea that if we don't behave in a certain way, we are not good daughters and sons. Despite our parents' wishes, at some point it may not be possible to keep them at home. A decision like this is heart-wrenching enough without commercials adding to our guilt.

When our loved one is feeling scared and vulnerable, we want to make them feel better. We feel guilty because they did so much for us so how can we deny them? We feel guilty that we can't fix the problem or take away their fear. In that guilt it is too easy to promise things you may not be able to fulfill. The only thing we know about the future that's for sure is that our loved one's health will change.

Of course, if your relationship with your parents was not one in which you felt nurtured, instead of guilt you may be feeling resentment. Resentment is a common emotion among caregivers, no matter what its source.

My parents worked hard to ensure that their home was set up (as much as possible) for them to age-in-place. I know my mother wants to, as she puts it, "leave this house feet first." But I have never promised her I will keep her in this house forever. I have promised that I would do my best to keep her home as long as possible.

The truth is, if my mother needed to be in a wheelchair full time, she couldn't stay in her home. Built in the late 1950s, the hallways and door openings are too small to navigate with a wheelchair, and renovating would require money we don't have. This is why, when she felt so vulnerable after my father died, she said, "I don't want to leave here; I'd be leaving your father." I said, "Mom, I will do everything in my power to keep you here, but I'm not going to promise you. We don't know what the future will bring. I need you to stay strong and keep mobile using your go-cart to get around the house so you can stay here."

Frustration

I get frustrated with my mother. There I said it.

- ♥ Waiting on her to finish getting ready so we can leave for an appointment is frustrating.
- ♥ Having her insist on having control of paperwork that will end up in my hands to deal with is frustrating.
- ♥ Having her put "away" the dishes at 11:00 p.m. at night is frustrating because, really, most things are left on the kitchen table for me to put away in the morning so I must deal with them before I can do anything else.

Isn't it interesting that the things I find frustrating are the things I perceive to be an inconvenience? When I view what my mother is doing through a different lens, one where these acts contribute to her quality of life and allow her to contribute to our family, my frustration lessons. Through that new lens:

- ♥ I recognize that it gives her such joy to get out of the house, even to a doctor's appointment, that putting on lipstick and perfume at the last minute makes her feel whole again.
- ♥ I understand that keeping control of the paperwork gives her a sense of independence and control over her life, which is so important given all the other losses.
- ♥ I'm grateful Mom is still healthy enough to contribute to our family by putting away the dishes.

Anger

No one can push my buttons like my mother. No one can make me angrier faster. After all we have years of history, and what drove me crazy when I was growing up didn't suddenly disappear. If anything, it makes me crazy faster. Why is she telling me what to do? I'm an adult, and I know how to load the dishwasher!

During these years as Mom's caregiver, I've learned that if I let frustrations pile up and I don't say something right away, I can go from zero to 100 on the anger meter in mere seconds And I'll confess it is my most challenging emotion because words spoken in anger can't be taken back.

I've also learned that what feels to me like control is really Mom's way of managing her world and keeping it in order. I make her pancakes every other weekend. Mom directing me on where to find the pancake mix, the pan to use, and the vanilla every time can send me over the edge. I must stop, take a breath, and remind myself that it is not because she thinks I'm incapable. When I told her how this makes me feel, she explained that she does it because she thinks she is helping me. Control or help? Either way I need to hear it differently and deal with that inner eight-year-old rebelling about being told what to do.

I know anger is normal. I know that expressing anger and not letting it pile up is healthier for both of us. I find it is easier to express my anger and talk about it rationally when my anger comes from frustration, stress, or exhaustion. What is harder to deal with is the anger I sometimes feel about being Mom's caregiver. The life I knew is gone. In the same way the life Mom knew with Dad is gone. It feels like I am no longer in control of my world, and I want to rail at the unfairness of it all. My plans are on hold because I don't know what the future will bring with Mom, and that makes me angry as well. Admitting to myself that I am angry at no longer being in control of my life has helped me understand Mom better. After all, she feels like her life is spinning out of control as well.

Am I angry all the time? No. This emotion comes and goes like all the others, but the anger I feel about the impact caregiving has on my life is not one I can express to Mom. At times she feels like she is a burden to me so why would I add to that hurt?

Neither one of us had control over losing Dad, but that monumental life change brought us to where we are today. Chances are you can and will get angry at fate and unexpected circumstances, but it doesn't change anything. Acknowledge the anger, do something about it if you can, express it in a positive way, but don't hold onto it. In letting go of my anger, I remember that Mom and I love each other. I remember there is a mother/daughter bond that neither one of us wants to lose because of angry words—words that can't be taken back. I empathize with Mom because she is feeling many of the same emotions that I am, and in that empathy love flourishes.

Resentment

Resentment often goes hand in hand with anger for me. There are times when I resent being Mom's hands-on caregiver every other weekend because it means missing church and missing out on plans friends are making. I even miss sleeping in my own bed. It drives me crazy that I must literally pack up my life and my dog for four days away from home every two weeks and every holiday.

The hardest part of being Mom's caregiver is that my life is no longer my own, and that is my biggest form of resentment. This realization happened early in our caregiving journey. I had plans to go to Atlantic City for a couple of days with friends. I had been at Moms for the weekend, staying an extra night so that her caregiver could go to her doctor Monday morning. Mom is fine on her own for a couple of hours so I'd left to go home and get ready to meet my friends. I knew that Mom's caregiver had been to her doctor earlier so we anticipated her getting back to Mom's within an hour of my leaving. I'm packed for the weekend, sitting in the driveway of my dog's daycare where he will board for the next two days, when the phone rings. It's my mother's caregiver. Her doctor is admitting her to the hospital. Seriously? Yes. And I resented it.

The first phone call was to my friends, cancelling my plans to join them. The second phone call was to my mother, letting her know what happened. The third phone call was to the daycare, letting them know that although I was sitting in the driveway, Josh was not going to be staying with them and why. Then I drove home, got more clothes, and drove back to my mother's where I was her caregiver for four days. It could have been an awful four days full of resentment but thankfully, by the time I'd gotten to Mom's, I had calmed down. I knew she would feel bad that my plans had to be cancelled, and I didn't want to add to it.

Getting past resentment takes work. I must remind myself that I chose the way we worked out my caregiving schedule, and I chose it for good reasons. I can choose to resent not being able to see my friends whenever I want, or I can choose to invite those friends to dinner with Mom and I the weekends I am with her.

The hardest part of getting past resentment for me is letting go of old hurts. The dialogue in my head around old hurts is comfortable and self-righteous. When I let that record in my head play repeatedly, it gets me nowhere. When I work to acknowledge and let go of resentments, I am calmer, more content, don't get angry and, most important, can remember that Mom and I are a team; we're in this together.

Grief

Grief is an emotion that doesn't get named in caregiving until our loved one dies. But anticipatory grief is common and rarely recognized or discussed. This type of grief is found in facing a coming loss. The loss may be the eventual death of a loved one; it may be the loss of dreams or your place in the world. It can even be the loss of financial stability.

Anticipatory grief can run through caregiving like a river for you and your caree. Placid until suddenly, when we least expect it, we hit the rapids. Sometimes we stay upright, and sometimes we are pulled underwater.

Truthfully, Mom and I share many of the same feelings of grief. Both of us grieve the letting go of expectations and our way of being in the world. There is grief as I see my mother age and realize our time together is on a downward trajectory. There is Mom's grief in her loss of independence, mobility, and health. And we share the grief of losing my father. My dad, my sounding board and biggest cheerleader, is gone. Mom has lost her husband and best friend.

Grief comes at the most unexpected time and places. Life was so chaotic after Dad died. There were so many financial and legal details to work out. I had to find Mom a live-in caregiver before I could travel again for work—all of which meant I had not had a chance to start grieving the loss of my father. About three months after he died, I remember walking into a store to buy a Mother's Day card. I had to walk right back out again because I was sobbing. In that moment I realized I would never buy my father another card. The wave of grief that came over me was like an undertow at the beach. I had to let it take me under and stay with it until I could come up for a breath of air.

Through that experience I've learned to allow grief to come over me. By that I mean feel the feeling. I'm learning not to numb it with busy work, food, or sleep. I've learned to talk about it with Mom and others. It was a few years before my mother could talk about my dad. I'm grateful we are in a place that she can say, "You know your father…" In that shared memory, in that new insight into their relationship, there is consolation and comfort. Even great joy.

Mom and I are still adjusting to this life, and because things change, acceptance comes in fits and starts. Fear still comes and goes with all the unknowns ahead of us. And I still find myself resenting what is yet to come and the impact it will have on my life, which makes me feel guilty. But this is the reality of being a caregiver.

Emotional intelligence

If there is ever a time that self-awareness is important, it is in your role as caregiver. Don't take on another person's stuff.

I am continually amazed by all the people that have an opinion on how things should work in your life as a caregiver. "Wouldn't your mother be better off in assisted living? She'd have more of a social life." "Why are you up at your mother's so much? I thought she has a live-in caregiver." Even this one: "You should make your brother come home more often and help you with your mother."

I do believe folks are trying to be helpful, but the options they offer are often ones they need or would work for their family. What they don't realize is how it can make us feel. If a comment or question results in you second-guessing yourself, take a step back. Is this a time when the question or comment is about their stuff, not yours? In our family my brother and I are in complete agreement on keeping Mom in her home and on the level and type of help he gives my mother. For many reasons he is unable to take part in the hands-on care, and we are both OK with it. I think comments like these can be about that person's family. Maybe they are frustrated that the division of labor among their siblings is uneven. Don't automatically take on another person's stuff; you have enough of your own.

One final thought on emotions

If I am feeling angry or resentful, too often I live in my head. By that I mean I have a complete conversation (fight) with this person, and they are not privy to it. Since I get to make up the script, every response I assign to them makes me angrier and angrier or more and more resentful. It's insanity.

At one point in my career I had an hour drive to my consulting client. I was furious with my boss over some situation. For the life of me I can't remember why I was so angry; I just stewed about it the entire drive in, arriving cranky and out of sorts. Not a good way to start your day. When I finally realized what I was doing, I thought: "This situation and person are taking up too much real estate in my head. I've got to focus on something else." But what? I love the beach and have always wanted to buy a piece of property on the ocean. So instead of obsessing about work, I decorated that entire beach house in my head while I was driving. It had a huge wraparound porch painted a light grey with big ceiling fans, wicker furniture, plants, and shades that could be pulled down in the heat of the day. There were three sets of French doors that opened to the porch from the kitchen, family room, and master suite. Each room in the house was painted a different shade of blue depending on the light in the room and taken from the sky and the ocean. Hard wood floors and big comfy casual furniture welcomed family and friends. In my head it was a sight to behold. And after several days of decorating the house instead of having a mental fight, I was over being angry. This was a great lesson for me as a caregiver. It pays to not live in your head.

Exercise Seven
Becoming Aware of Your Emotions

Try to find a quite space and time to sit down and reflect on your seven emotions that come up during caregiving. This is not the time to shy away from how you are really feeling. Don't self-edit. Your emotions are YOUR emotions. Give yourself the gift of dispassionately naming them.

Then create a list of the times and situations that bring up these emotions. Include a complete description of what happened, possible causes, what you said or did in that moment. Again, don't self-edit.

This is not a one and done exercise. Be prepared to add other situations to this list as time goes on and life changes for you and your loved one.

Sample Emotion Worksheet

Emotion	Description, Time and Place	Cause	My Reaction	Insight
Anger	We had a 9:00 a.m. doctor appointment; I had to be at Dad's house by 8:30 and leave by 8:45 to be on time	A trip to the bathroom at the last minute made us late	I started yelling at Dad; made Dad feel like a child, and I felt guilty	Dad moves slowly so build extra time into our schedule and make appoint-ments later if possible
Frustration	Dining room, working at the computer, mid-afternoon	Mom keeps asking me questions while I'm trying to work	My answers keep getting shorter and shorter	Mom was worried about an upcoming visitor but explain why I can't have this conversa-tion right now, then set a boundary for a time we can talk after work

Then ask yourself these questions:

- ♥ Was I particularly stressed by outside factors when this emotion appeared, or did caregiving create the stress and the emotion followed?
- ♥ In retrospect, did this situation remind me of something that happened in my childhood? At work? In my marriage?
- ♥ Does this emotion come up repeatedly? Under what circumstances does it appear? Is there a trigger (person or place) that brings this emotion up?

Once you get better at recognizing your emotions, it makes it possible to take a step back and, right then and there, rein them in or express them in a more appropriate way.

Chapter 4
Having Hard Conversations

I don't like confrontation. Most of us don't. Nor do we like facing emotions like anger, vulnerability, or sadness, and we don't like reliving times when we've been hurt. As caregivers we may be surprised when our words create an unintended confrontation. We don't WANT to confront, upset, or hurt our loved one. But the truth is, a hard conversation with our elderly parents often does feel like a confrontation, and it will bring up difficult emotions. It is so much easier to avoid talking about a hard topic than it is to think about it, plan for it, and take the conversational plunge at the best possible time.

For me, I've learned when I don't prepare and make the time to have a discussion my resentment builds. Instead of a supportive conversation it can quickly escalate into a shouting match or a freezing out with the loudest sound of all—silence. The worst case is a relationship broken beyond repair.

In Chapter One I shared with you a conversation Mom and I had about secrets. It was the first of many difficult conversations over the past five years. It is still not easy to bring up a subject that makes us feel vulnerable, angry, or sad, but we are getting better and better at it. Through practice we have learned we can get to the other side of an issue with our relationship intact. The bottom line is that we choose to be a team.

In this chapter we are going to discuss the best way to plan for and structure those hard conversations. We will focus on language, time, place, and motivation.

It's never too late

It doesn't matter if you are new to caregiving or you've been at caregiving a while; it is never too late to learn a new way of talking about difficult subjects. In the same way it is never too late to start on your caregiver contract. You are, after all, working to break old patterns and forge new ones, and let me remind you: Creating new behaviors is possible. Remember Mom going to a family birthday party without me?

Here is another example. The last time I was with Mom she started a conversation that I know was difficult for her. It made her feel vulnerable. In her courage to approach the subject we were able to create a new way of being together that works better for her, and it doesn't make me feel guilty about the solution.

Mom's TV is in her den, and that requires going down two steps. For months now, I would ask if she'd like to watch her favorite programs. I say "watch" but what I really mean is she listens to them using special earphones. This entire time she has said, "No, I think I'll read my book (e.g., listen to her books on tape). You go down to the den and watch TV." I knew something was going on but didn't push her. When she was ready to tell me, she would. I must admit it was frustrating to me because I knew she enjoyed this time together, and I felt guilty about watching TV without her.

The breaking point came the weekend Joe Biden announced he was running for president. Mom loves Joe Biden so I knew she would want to see him on one of our favorite programs. I invited her to watch it with me, and she said "yes." When I let her know that the taped program was ready, she got quiet and then said, "I have something to tell you. I'm scared to death of going down the steps into the den."

Now I had suggested more than once that we think about moving the TV into the living room, and those same words were on the tip of my tongue. Then she said, "Maybe I can sit in the dining room on a chair with the headphones on. I can't see the TV anyway." Wow, that solution had never occurred to me! It was easy to move a comfortable chair into position, make sure the headphones worked, and start the program. We thoroughly enjoyed it together.

We continued to watch TV until sitting in that chair became uncomfortable, at which point Mom said, "I wish the headphones worked while I'm sitting in the living room." Guess what? They do.

Mom got situated in her comfy spot on the couch, her dog next to her, wrapped in her favorite soft blanket, and we "watched" TV together. Despite not being in the same room, we were close enough to talk about the shows while I skipped past commercials or queued up another program. At the end of the night, Mom said, "It's been such a long time since I heard those voices."

It had been a long time since we watched TV together, and I did not realize how much I missed this shared activity. I'm grateful that she was willing to be honest and tell me her fear; in that vulnerability we made yet another adjustment to our contract.

Name the change you need

Loved ones are not mind readers.

In an earlier chapter I shared that watching TV with Mom was one of the social outlets that bound us together. When we lost that piece of our relationship for a while, it was hard for me not to push her and hard to respect the decision to keep the TV in the den. By the same token, it was hard for her to tell me why she was avoiding watching her favorite programs. Ultimately, when the time was right, when the motivation was right, she felt safe enough to tell me her fears.

If you don't name the change, you won't find a way to create the change. Naming a change means looking within yourself to determine what is making you feel vulnerable, anxious, angry, or resentful. Then it's a matter of finding the right opportunity, time, and place to bring up the topic so you can have a productive discussion and figure out a new way of doing things.

Discuss the change you need

The time and place need to be right in order to be heard.

Mom's willingness to tell me about her fear, despite feeling vulnerable, allowed us to figure out a new way to watch TV together. In discussing how to make it happen we advanced and discarded several ideas. Which chair should I bring into the dining room for her to sit on in comfort? Where is the best place to put the chair so she has something to hold onto when it is time to get out of it? Together we figured out a new way to keep our social bond and watch our favorite programs, and we laughed every time I had to remind her to take the headphones off so we could talk.

It was Mom's willingness to share her fears with me, to name the change she needed, that allowed us to renegotiate this part of our contract. It was my willingness to not push her about moving the TV, even though I thought it was a perfect solution. In the end, Mom trusted that I would listen to her fears, and that together we would work to find a solution. This is how a caregiver contract evolves.

How do you get to trust?

I'll be honest with you: Building trust takes work and time. We have been practicing for the last five years to find a way to work together that is different from the original mother/daughter relationship contract. I've learned there are four pieces that must work in tandem to have productive conversations and ultimately lead to trust. They are language, time, place, and motivation.

Language: Rules of engagement

In Chapter Two we talked about conversation nonstarters such as "You must... You should... You need to..." The other set of conversation nonstarters are: "You always...., You never..., You don't...." When emotions such as anger or resentment are running high, it's never a good idea to start a conversation in which the other person feels attacked.

Remember the rules of fair fighting:
1. Figure out why you're upset before you start the discussion.
2. Discuss the issue at hand. Don't bring past hurts or fights into this discussion.
3. Be respectful in words and tone of voice. No yelling.
4. Avoid words like never or always; they generalize the conversation and that doesn't work.
5. Take time out if things start to feel as if they are getting out of hand.

And most important of all:
6. Express your feelings with words, and take responsibility for your feelings.

I recently had a conversation with my mother around a family event. That conversation is not finished, but I was in the car driving while we were having it so time and place were not right.

We are invited to a family wedding on one of the Saturdays when I am not her caregiver. Since Mom doesn't get the opportunity to be with family often, it is important to both of us that she goes. The problem is she wants me to stay at her house after the event but I want to go home. For the first time I am hearing she will not go if I don't spend that night at her house; otherwise, she will worry about me driving late at night. I'm starting to feel manipulated and angry as we're having this conversation.

"Mom, I'm frustrated that you won't go if I don't promise to stay at your house that night. You just said you don't get to see this part of the family often, and now you're saying it doesn't matter if you go. I know that is not true."

Her response: "Well, there is still time to decide."

I still felt frustrated and manipulated, and now I felt guilty as well. Here's the thing: My mother is a champion worrier. I used to feel guilty when she worried because I was traveling for work or driving in bad weather to a meeting. I was sure I had resolved not taking this guilt on because no matter what, she will worry. I can't change who she is. But this feels different because this type of social outlet is what binds our relationship contract together. I'm not sure how we will resolve it. I only know we have not finished this aggravating conversation.

I am sharing this exchange because it is a good example of how the rules of fair fighting are applied to conversations.

- ♥ I could feel myself getting angry. I had to stop talking in order to figure out that I was feeling manipulated and frustrated by her position.
- ♥ It was important that I tell her how I felt; in other words, "I'm feeling frustrated" but not "You always do this."
- ♥ Continuing the conversation was futile. It was not the right time or place, and she was right: We didn't have to decide right then.

I suspect that I will stay the night to ensure that Mom goes to the event. And that is OK this time. What's not OK is if I continue to feel manipulated and resentful. It's on me to figure out where these emotions originate. How much of this is me being angry that Dad is gone? How much is tied into my resentment that my life is no longer my own? How much is my inner eight-year-old knee-jerk reaction in feeling that I'm not in control?

Once I figure it out, once I get some distance from our first conversation, I will be better prepared to have another one. Who knows? My ultimate answer may be that I can't control her worrying so despite not fulfilling my end of our social contract this time, it's her choice not to go.

Find the right time and place—multiple times

Mom is right: There is time to decide about both of us attending the wedding. More importantly, that moment while I was driving was not the right time. I had been out all day. I was frustrated by traffic, road repairs, an accident, and the short window of time I had to get home and get back out the door for another meeting. If we had continued the conversation then, it would not have gone well.

In the heat of the moment it may be hard not to jump right in. If you can't help yourself and the discussion starts to escalate, remember rule five in fighting fair: Take a time-out.

Finding the right time also means being sensitive to what is going on with your loved one. If he or she is not feeling well, or is already in a bad mood, is this really the best time to start a discussion? Unfortunately, it may be the best time because it is the only opportunity you will have. If it is the only opportunity, the rules of engagement are even more important.

The right time can be dictated by the right place. Driving with most people, regardless of age, is often a time they will open up and tell you about their day. And it is a good time to ask the questions that will give you a clue about what is going on in their lives. Mom and I have some of our best discussions on long drives. The intimacy of that small space lends itself to talking, and such conversations do not involve eye contact, making them easier. We are usually headed somewhere fun so we are both in a good mood, which helps. An afternoon of cooking together is another good time for us. It brings back warm memories of my childhood and reignites our mother/daughter bond instead of our time being focused on caregiving. Some of the most natural times for our discussions occur when I am engaged in an act that involves intimacy. By that I mean cutting her hair or doing her nails. The intimacy of touch opens both of us up to really listening to what the other person is saying.

Combing someone's hair before you answer a question or make a point slows down the discussion so that it can be thoughtful, not a lashing out.

My favorite communication technique is the "Drip Method." This is when I bring up a topic more than once and in multiple settings. It works well with my mother for all types of conversations. Let me share a funny story about Mom and the Drip Method. I need to preface this story with the fact that my brother and his wife live about 12 hours away.

I had approached the subject of getting Mom an Amazon Alexa several times. The first time her response was: "Not in my house. I have no need for anything like that, and I wouldn't know how to use it." The second time I brought it up we were in the living room, not in the kitchen. My mother had just expressed how frustrated she was in trying to dial cell phone numbers for family members. When Dad was alive, he had purchased a phone system that allowed for up to 60 two-digit phone numbers. Unfortunately, the phone system is over 30 years old, and the knowledge of how to reassign a two-digit number to a ten-digit phone number died with him. I approached the subject of getting an Alexa by telling her that with this assistive technology, I could program Alexa to recognize cell phone numbers. All she would have to say is "Alexa, call Pat." Again, she was not enthusiastic about the idea. The third time I reminded her about the cell phone numbers she didn't say "no" immediately; she asked me more about how Alexa would work and what she could do with it besides call people. Fast forward a couple of weeks and we are visiting my aunt, a contemporary of my mother and the proud owner of an Alexa. Taking the opportunity, I ask my aunt how she likes Alexa.

"Oh, I love it. I can ask it anything. Alexa, what time is it? Alexa what's the weather? You try it, Deb."

"Alexa, play a Benny Goodman song," I said. I didn't say one word about how Alexa worked or ask if she liked it while we were on the way home.

Days later we were sitting in the living room when Mom says, "That Alexa thing that Pat has. If I ask it what Kevin is doing, will it tell me?"

I admit I had to stop to make sure I didn't giggle, and then explained that Alexa couldn't see what Kevin was doing so it couldn't tell us. End of discussion. Another couple of weeks go by when we are asked to be part of an assistive technology pilot program with the United Way of Northern New Jersey. Once again, I approach the subject of Alexa, but this time I'm prepared. I explain to Mom that we can get an Alexa Echo Dot as part of a pilot project. If we like it, we can keep it. Mom's immediate response: "Oh no, I don't want that in my house. Besides, where would I put it?" Voila! I whip an Echo Dot out of the package, put it in her hands, and say: "See how small it is? We can put it on the end table in the living room. It won't be in the way, and it will be right near where you sit." Mom still wasn't convinced.

Then the coup de grace. It was free. If we didn't like it, we could send it back anytime during the next three months. If we liked it, we kept it.

Mom said: "Well, if it's free…"

The end of this story is that Mom does not use Alexa to call relatives or friends. I had not considered that calling someone with Alexa results in a conversation that is not private. She is uncomfortable with using it when her caregiver is around, and I understand. But guess what? Alexa has given her a sense of independence she hasn't had in years. I bought two smart plugs for the lamps in the living room. Now she can say: "Alexa, turn on lamp one." She no longer sits in the dark until either the caregiver or I can come turn on the lights. She is tickled pink and has asked for the same technology for her bedroom. I've got it covered.

Motivation: You can't force another person to change

The two keys to getting seniors to change a decision or attitude are control and knowing what motivates them. In Mom's case, socializing with family and giving me respite with my friends was important enough that she was willing to change her mind and trust someone else to take her to the party. In the case of Alexa, getting something for free was the key.

Mom had control over keeping Alexa, and she had control over saying "yes" to my cousin bringing her to the family gathering. In giving her control by using the right language and motivation, we both won.

The two most dreaded conversations

Particularly difficult conversations—the ones nobody wants to have with their loved one—are the subjects of driving a car and moving out of their home.

The best example I can give you for changing a conversation on moving from "no" to a "go" comes from *How to Say It to Seniors*. It has all the elements of what it takes to have a successful conversation on a difficult topic.

I'm going to paraphrase how the author describes the family situation. The adult children want their mother to move out of her house because the bedroom and bathroom are upstairs, and she can no longer navigate the stairs safely. All demands fall on deaf ears: "You need to move out of this house. It's not safe. What if you fall?" "You can't stay here; you can't go up and down the stairs like you used to." When the family gave Mom control and changed their language, it looked like this: "Mom, I'm worried about you going up and down the stairs to go to the bathroom. I know you want to stay here. In order to do keep you safe, let's put a bathroom and bedroom downstairs." After thinking about it for a couple of days, Mom came back to the family and said: "Putting money into this old house to renovate for a bath and bedroom down here isn't worth it. I'll never get the money back I put into it. Let's sell it and look at Assisted Living."

♥ Language: I'm worried.
♥ Control: I know you want to stay here.
♥ Motivation: It's not worth putting money into this old house.

Driving a car is a trickier conversation if your loved one is putting other people at risk. Giving up keys is a tangible loss of independence. Many seniors resist even engaging in a conversation about not driving.

If it's a must-have conversation, what motivates your loved one? Is it finances? With the right language, motivation, and control, the initial conversation might sound like this: "My car insurance just went up again. Has yours gone up as well? And the cost of gas is almost three dollars a gallon. Between that, insurance, and maintenance on my car, it's expensive. Are the expenses of keeping a car one you want to continue to pay going forward? Now there is

Uber, Lyft, and other public transportation options that are much less expensive. Would you like to investigate these with me?"

If finances are not a motivator, then the conversation may need to change to your parent's ability to drive. During a conversation in which you express your concern about driving at night, suggesting a Mature Drivers Evaluation may help. This will check reflexes, vision, motor control, and other factors of safe driving. The risk is that your senior passes, despite your desire that he or she stop driving.

If multiple conversations don't help, it may require the intervention of a doctor. I would have a conversation with the doctor prior to bringing up the subject with your parent so that you can express your concerns privately. The last thing you want is for the doctor to ask your loved one, "Are you still okay driving?" Of course, they will say "yes," and you have lost the opportunity. If this is still not enough motivation, many states will honor the confidentiality if an unsafe driver is reported. They may require your loved one to take a test. Of course, the last resort is to take the car keys or remove the vehicle.

I admit I'm grateful that I don't need to have this conversation with my mother. She gave up driving years ago.

The other conversation no one wants to have

Conversations that center on legal documents can be difficult as well. If you are not yet caught in the whirlwind of caregiving, now is the time to practice using your hard conversation skills. Money and health are, for many families, taboo subjects. I am here to tell you that two critical documents need to be in place as soon as possible. They are Durable Power of Attorney (POA) for finances and Power of Attorney for Healthcare. Both documents are critical for your parents and for you as the caregiver. A sibling or another trusted family member can serve in those roles if that is preferred. What is important is that you have the conversations. This is one topic in which the Drip Method may be the only way to make progress.

What are we willing to do (or not do) for one another?

Not everything is about having a hard conversation and changing your caregiver contract. Some things you simply must "do" as a caregiver—whether you do them willingly or not.

Mom will ask me to check the garage freezer for a frozen vegetable she thinks is in there. Now we have three freezers. At best there is a 50/50 chance that what she is looking for is in that freezer. Nothing makes me crazier than wasting time hunting for something. It's a frustration that has roots in my childhood. As a child, I would take my time getting up or whine, "Why can't Kevin do it? You always make me stop what I'm doing." As an adult, sometimes I'm gracious about it (willing) and sometimes I am ungracious (unwilling). The bottom line is she can't do it so I must.

The truth is family dynamics influence us long after we are adults. Differences in how siblings were treated, differences in expectations for daughters versus sons, differences in how a painful subject was approached by our parents all influence our caregiving role. It stands to reason that what we are willing or not willing to do for one another, and the way we carry out caregiver tasks, has roots in these early years.

Mom and I struggled to find common ground during my childhood. As adults, we've had to let go of the unrealistic expectations we have for one another. On the other hand, my relationship with my father was easy. Dad and I were a lot alike and functioned well as a team. He often served as the intermediary, helping Mom and me to deal better with one another. Now that he is gone, we've had to discover new, healthy ways to be together. It helps that I now understand old family patterns. It allows me to be deliberate about not reacting the same way I did as a child. Knowledge is power and the beginning of change. With an understanding of childhood family dynamics, I have insight into the "why" of my emotions. The "why" helps me find the right conversational words and to ensure I have realistic expectations. It is this knowledge that I call on to renegotiate our caregiver relationship contract.

How do we support one another?

I'm an extravert until I'm an introvert. When I have a busy week networking for work, guests at my house for a couple of days, or just a weekend like this last one with no downtime, I need space and quiet time. When a Mom weekend comes at the tail end of insanity, it makes it hard because I AM her social interaction. What I must do is tell her what I need up front that first night: "Mom, I'm wiped out. Can we just be together tonight and deal with the list of things for me to do tomorrow?"

Having this conversation instead of giving her monosyllabic answers goes a long way to keeping our relationship on an even keel.

Exercise Eight
Strategies for a Hard Conversation

1. Start by looking within yourself to determine what is making <u>you</u> feel vulnerable, anxious, angry, or resentful about this situation. Decide if it is really your own problem or something that does need to be discussed.
2. Write down all the possible motivations your loved one may have for making a particular change or accepting a boundary.
3. List the places you and your loved one feel safe together. Is it while playing cards, going for a walk, or driving somewhere?
4. Plan the best time to initiate the conversation. Is it when they first get up, over a meal, or while involved in an act that involves touch like cutting hair? Be sensitive to what is going on with your loved one. If he or she is not feeling well, or is already in a bad mood, put the conversation off.
5. Decide what language to use that gives your loved one some control over the situation or change.

Enlist the help of others:

♥ Create a list of people your loved one trusts. It may be a family member closer in age, a close friend, or someone from their faith community. When you approach this person, explain your concern, the best possible outcome from your point of view, and ask if they have any advice or would be willing to broach the subject with your loved one. If they don't share your concern or are uncomfortable with starting the conversation, let it go or ask someone else.

Exercise Nine
Practice a Hard Conversation

1. Decide in your head the issue at hand and practice expressing your feelings in respectful words and tone of voice.
2. Express yourself with "I" words. "I feel hurt" or "I feel frustrated," not "You say hurtful things" or "You are so mean."
3. Listen for overgeneralizations that bring past fights or hurts into the conversation and nip it in the bud.
4. Stop if you hear yourself use the words "always" or "never."
5. Take a breath if you feel yourself tensing up and speaking more quickly or loudly.
6. Be aware of when you are getting emotional and feeling out of control. Stop the conversation and come back to it after you have calmed down.
7. Take responsibility for your feelings and actions.

Once you know what motivates your loved one, what language will give them control, the time and place where you will both feel safe and you have practiced the conversation, go for it!

Chapter 5

Understanding Expectations
And Setting Boundaries

Are you a people pleaser?

Are you the family peacemaker?

Are you constantly apologizing for things you can't control?

Then my guess is, like me, you have a hard time setting boundaries. I'm a recovering people pleaser. I say recovering because I still fight to listen to my inner voice telling me it's a bad idea to say "yes" to a request. I know if I say "yes," I'll feel manipulated. When I feel manipulated, I get resentful, and that affects my attitude, my communication style, and my interactions with the person. It is hard to say "no" to those you love, but it is one of the highest forms of self-love.

I'm also a recovering family peacemaker. As a child, nothing would upset me more than yelling and angry emotions. In my quest to avoid confrontations, I took on the role of always trying to smooth the waters. Too often I still try to make sure everyone is happy. But in holding onto this role, I am often overextended, and my own well-being is put aside. Maybe it is an outgrowth of empathy, but when I try to fix the pain of another person it is at great cost to myself, and that is the direct opposite of self-care. I'm still empathetic, but I'm learning not to take on someone else's pain and try to fix them or their problems.

Then there is triangulation. That's when someone (Mom) doesn't want to talk to someone (her caregiver) so I am expected to relay messages between them. I still get caught in this trap. I know better, yet there are times when I will be the third person in a conversation just to keep the peace. It's a bad idea. As the third person in a two-person conversation, it lets the other two get away with passive-aggressive behavior, which never resolves the situation and most often escalates it.

As a people pleasing peacemaker, I often feel responsible for things that are completely out of my control. And when I feel responsible I find myself apologizing. Because of this, I've decided to build up a "not my issue" muscle. Developing this muscle is helping me to recognize that I don't have to take responsibility for someone else's problem, take on their expectations, or say "yes" to every request.

If you're a woman and a caregiver, I suspect you may also be a people pleasing peacemaker. Here's the good news: Co-creating a caregiver relationship contract forces you to be aware of when you are saying "yes" when "no" is the right answer. This process allows you to let go of the peacemaking role because your caree is held responsible for his or her own actions. And when you don't feel responsible for everything, you do a lot less apologizing.

Expectations for others

Before we talk about setting boundaries, I'd like to talk about expectations. We live our lives shaped by expectations— expectations that are usually based on our assumptions. We assume loved ones will act in a certain way. We assume everyone else will handle a situation the same way we would.

It stands to reason that your caree will have assumptions about your role as his or her caregiver. On the flip side are the assumptions you have about your caregiver role. Because expectations are often unspoken, they can be difficult to bring into the open and discuss. But if we don't discuss them, it is easy to hold someone to an unrealistic expectation or a standard they did not know existed.

Assumptions about our caregiver role are based on several things: birth order, gender, and familial role. Because these are embedded in the fabric of your family, it can be difficult to challenge and change the assumptions. The most common assumption people make is that the daughter, daughter-in-law, or sister will be the primary caregiver. I find in my work with caregivers that this expectation is the number one cause of family conflict.

My expectation has always been that I would be the primary caregiver for my parents. It shaped my life. I made the decision to move back to New Jersey to be closer to them. I made the decision to live within an hour of their home so I could be there quickly in an emergency. I made the push to structure my consulting work so that it was mobile, allowing me to work from anywhere. All these decisions gave me the ability to live with my parents the last months of Dad's life and while getting Mom settled.

You may not have the ability to move closer to your loved ones. You may not have a job that allows for flexible start and end times, or one that is open to working offsite. We have a lot of work ahead of us to educate businesses and governments about the importance of keeping highly trained and good workers through job sharing, flexible hours that allow for caregiving duties, and mobile working arrangements. How helpful would it be if the norm was to allow an employee two to three hours over lunch for a doctor's appointment or to make phone calls? Work would still get completed; folks would just work later or come in earlier.

As a new caregiver, the first expectation I had to deal with had nothing to do with my job. It was Mom's unspoken expectation that life would continue with no changes to her routines. It took me a while to even recognize there was a problem. But once I did, we were able to work on changing the dynamic. Here is what happened.

Over the years my parents had developed morning and bedtime routines. I realized during Dad's first hospital stay that Mom's unspoken expectation was that I would continue to keep them up. After all, she was comfortable with them so why would she expect anything to change? As for me, why wouldn't I continue them? I was new to my role as her caregiver and assumed this is the way things must be done.

It quickly became apparent that Mom's expectations and mine were not going to work. During the two weeks Dad was in the hospital I worked full time out of my parents' home, which meant I was working between hospital visits and until past midnight most nights. In addition, I made sure I was with Dad for breakfast and doctor rounds, then again for dinner. On top of that schedule I was Mom's caregiver, responsible for grocery shopping, laundry, cleaning, putting out garbage, and recycling—really all the tasks at their house. Then there were daily walks for my dog and my parents' dog.

One night, sitting right next to her, I fell asleep watching TV. I mean I was asleep. My mother could not wake me—not by calling my name, not by shaking the chair with her cane. It wasn't until the dogs started barking that I woke up, a good ten minutes after my mother had initially tried to wake me. It scared both of us. This was when I started to realize that I could not continue caring for Mom exactly as Dad had cared for her—at least not if I was going to keep my sanity and my health.

Given the amount of time I was putting in, by the time bedtime rolled around I was beyond exhausted. But before I could go to sleep, I had to take Mom's blood sugar, put in her eyedrops, and get what she needed to brush her teeth. Then, in the bedroom, make sure the curtains were closed, the bed turned down, and that she had clothes for the morning and water by her bedside. This was my parents' contract for a bedtime ritual.

Every night I could feel myself tense up and get angry at everything I had to do before I could go to bed. Finally, not long after the sleeping incident, I said, "Mom, can we talk? I am exhausted and overwhelmed. We need to change something in the routine to get you ready for bed. It would be helpful if I didn't have to bring everything you need to brush your teeth into the kitchen each night. Can we find a place where we can store it?" For some reason, that one task—carrying things from the bathroom to the kitchen and back again—made my head explode. Every. Single. Night.

Once I brought this out into the open, Mom was willing to make the change to our routine so together we figured out the best place to keep everything. Taking that one task off my plate helped me physically and mentally. Later she took over putting in her own eye drops. Mom's willingness to change was a blessing and opened a door to solving more problems together.

For me, the hardest part of challenging and changing expectations is recognizing them. You may find this as well. It may be because of the role you play in the family, because you are the oldest and the "responsible" one, or because you are a woman. It is hard when we're in crisis mode or in the trenches of caregiving to recognize what is going on around us. We are so focused on dealing with the current problem or getting everything completed on our "to-do" list that we don't take a breath and think about what we are doing or how we are doing it.

Who has put their expectations on you? Is it your siblings, your boss, or society's expectation that women are the de facto caregivers?

Expectations for ourselves

The expectations we have for ourselves may be the most unrealistic. Let's face it: As caregivers, we are often our own worst enemy. How often do you feel responsible for making everything better—especially if your loved one is feeling vulnerable or scared, or your child or spouse is feeling neglected? How often do you say "yes" when you don't have the time to fulfill the request? Even more importantly, when you don't have the desire to fulfill the request?

Too often we feel guilty, and that keeps us locked into "should and must." I should be able to finish cooking for Mom before I must leave to pick up the kids from practice. I should be able to squeeze in Dad's doctor appointment over lunch and get back in time for my meeting. Instead of locking into the "should/must" mindset, stop and ask yourself, "Can I really continue to be the spouse/parent/ employee/friend that I was before adding caregiver to this list? What needs to change? Where can I get help?"

There is another type of expectation that comes into play as caregivers. That is the expectation for our future. You may have been making plans to retire out of state or to take a cruise for three months. When we become caregivers, we often must let go of these expectations, or work for solutions during our absence. There is a natural grief that must be dealt with in letting our dreams and plans be put on hold or having to let them go.

Life-draining expectations

All of us have a way of operating in the world that makes us comfortable, makes us feel alive. For my friend Anna, her father was confrontational and liked to engage in banter that was just this side of nasty and argumentative. It was comfortable for him; it was the way he had interacted with her mom. In his early 90s when he came to live with Anna and her family, he naturally expected to continue this behavior. For weeks he tried to engage Anna in the same way, but she found this life-draining. She refused to engage with him when he spoke to her in a nasty or argumentative way.

When I asked her how she did it, "Years of therapy taught me to recognize it and to say, 'I'm not having this conversation' and walk away." In walking away, Anna set a clear boundary and changed an old family dynamic. Now, Dad rarely tries to engage her in this type of conversation but when he does, she continues to enforce her boundary. Anna's decision to not engage with her father when he was argumentative shows just how expectations and boundaries are tied together. It shows how setting a boundary, and sticking to it, can change behavior.

Setting boundaries

"Don't expect to feel good about every decision. Making decisions is like setting boundaries. You have to do it, but it will never feel good."

Anne Tumlinson, Founder of Daughterhood.org

Anne Tumlinson is right: It doesn't feel good to set boundaries, but it is necessary. I don't shy away from it like I did when I first became Mom's caregiver, but it is still hard.

Given that expectations are both spoken and unspoken, it may be easier to recognize a boundary has been crossed when your loved one makes a request.

Or is it a demand? I admit there are times when Mom is asking me to do something and I hear it as a demand. Do you have a knee-jerk reaction to requests/demands? I often do, and it pays to keep in mind that the issue we have with our loved one may be our issue, not theirs. The truth is, given our shared history, we know how to push one another's buttons, and we often feed off one another. As the saying goes, "It takes two to tango."

When Mom makes a request and the hair on the back of my neck goes up, I try to stop and not immediately react. Do you ever have a conversation in your head before you answer someone? I do, and it sounds like this: "Is this something I must do? Is this something I must do this very minute? **Is this a 'No, but' situation?** 'No, I can't take inventory of the freezer today, but I will schedule in time for the next weekend I'm with you.'"

Setting a boundary around unspoken expectations can be more difficult because we may not immediately recognize when a situation requires a boundary. After a while the pattern becomes clear, recognition hits, and it's like a lightbulb going off in our heads.

Spoken or unspoken, one way to recognize out of line expectations are your emotions. They are a good barometer for when a boundary has been crossed. As women's empowerment coach Crystal Andrus Morissette has said: "When you feel yourself becoming angry, resentful, or exhausted, pay attention to where you haven't set a healthy boundary."

Why do we find it difficult to set boundaries?

Clients have told me they fear that if they say "no" to their loved one, it will cause a rift in the relationship. There are compassionate ways to say "no" that allow for both parties to feel heard and validated. The question becomes this: Is this fear left over from childhood? You have the right as an adult to set boundaries that are different from your childhood. Are you feeling unheard? The communication strategies for hard conversations work in setting boundaries as well.

For me, the inability to set boundaries has a lot to do with guilt. I felt guilty that I was not going to be Mom's live-in caregiver. I feel guilty when my "to-do" list takes priority over spending time together the weekends I'm with Mom. But guilt is a terrible reason to say "yes" when "no" is the answer you need to give.

Mom was so sad and vulnerable after Dad died so telling her "no" felt impossible. At the same time, I was so overwhelmed it was hard for me to figure out what my boundaries were, let alone try to set them. You want to make your loved one's life as easy as possible during difficult times. But when their life is difficult, ours is as well, and chances are we don't recognize how sad and vulnerable we are feeling.

For a long time, part of keeping Mom in a better place meant I continued to keep bits and pieces of Dad's contract with her. Dad rarely told Mom "no," and that often frustrated me while he was alive. I wanted him to recognize his own needs and put himself first, at least some of the time. It can take us a while to see that we are falling into the same unhealthy patterns, can't it? Oddly enough, it was grocery shopping that made me realize that was exactly what I was doing.

We caregivers take on a multitude of Instrumental Activities of Daily Living (IADLs) for our loved ones (see Chapter Two). Grocery shopping every two weeks is one of mine. Where we live, the sales end on Saturday, and the new ones start on Sunday. Mom was used to Dad grocery shopping weekly, and she found it a difficult adjustment to think about what was needed for two weeks instead of one. We had fallen into a pattern of looking at both flyers to determine what was on sale each week. That meant I often found myself grocery shopping on both Saturday and Sunday. But it was on a Sunday when I found myself back at the grocery store for a third time in a weekend that I realized I had to say "no" to multiple trips. Setting this boundary was important; without it, I had little or no time for myself on a caregiving weekend.

"Mom, going to the grocery store three times in one weekend is exhausting for me. We don't get to spend time together, and I don't get a chance to catch my breath. From now on, if we forget to put something on our list, we need to let it go or I will pick it up while I'm at home and bring it to you the next time I come back." Not only did Mom hear me, but from that moment on while we are going over the two weekly flyers, she has said, "I don't want you running back and forth to the grocery store over the weekend. I don't need it that badly." Sometimes I do go back on a Sunday, but it is my choice. Often I will pick up what she needs while I'm at home and hold onto it until I see her again. Our adjustment to how we handle grocery shopping works better for both of us. Because I am no longer resentful, if I see something when I'm out and about that she might like or need, I call her, buy it, and bring it to her.

As a caregiver, don't be surprised if your loved one feels disappointed, angry, or hurt that you are changing the rules of the game when you set a boundary. By continuing to go the grocery store multiple times in one weekend I was enabling this expectation and contributing to the problem. A request to change something that is ongoing can feel as if it is coming out of the blue to our parents, making it important to structure a boundary conversation so that the new expectation is clear and heard.

The interesting thing about setting boundaries is that we get to flex the same muscles we use for hard conversations—and it takes the same courage.

Setting boundaries IS a hard conversation

In previous chapters we talked about avoiding the "should" and "must" language that is so easy to fall into. Nothing will stop a conversation, start a fight, or ensure your parent will not engage with you than starting with "You must/need to..." or "You always/never." When setting a boundary, it helps to apply the rules for fair fighting from Chapter Four and add these communication techniques.

♥ Setting boundaries requires being honest and direct.
♥ Don't make excuses for your feelings and needs.
♥ If you are going to be heard when setting a boundary, then address the problem when you are not angry.
♥ Don't use language that judges the request your loved one made.
♥ Don't use language that blames them.
♥ If you can, walk away until you are calm so that your tone of voice and energy don't convey anger, judgment, or blame.
♥ It helps to remember that it takes two to tango so taking a moment allows you to consider what you are bringing to this situation.
♥ Start the conversation with language that expresses love and caring.
♥ While you are learning how to build up a boundary setting muscle, it helps to start with something small but still important, like refusing to go the grocery store multiple times in one weekend.

Strategies to set boundaries in a loving and caring way

Why do we feel like we have to say "yes" when we don't have the time or desire to fulfill it? Sometimes we say "yes" to avoid a conflict. If you choose your battles carefully, this can be an effective strategy. But a better strategy when you're learning how to set a boundary is to buy yourself the time to say "no." "I'll think about it and get back to you" is a great response.

If you have no intention of fulfilling a request, then offer an alternative:

♥ "I can't help you but let me put you in touch with someone else."

♥ "No, I won't be able to go to the grocery store again today. But I'll text our neighbor who shops on Monday and ask her to pick up the bananas."

Because we bring our own bias to these conversations or we feel like we must do it all, many of my clients are surprised that offering an alternative, even if it is different from the expectation, will be enough for their loved one. Truly, the more we say "no," the easier it becomes. And when we say "no" with compassion, our loved one is less likely to see it as a reflection on them.

The first time I set a boundary with Mom was a doozy. Given what I know now, I would have handled it differently in terms of timing and the way I expressed it. But this boundary still impacts our caregiver relationship contract, and it changed how Mom and I relate to one another.

During those first couple of weeks after Dad died Mom and I were on autopilot. Like anyone who has lost a loved one, the immediate decisions around planning a funeral and wake and all the legal and financial work that had to be taken care of were all we could focus on.

Without time to grieve or recover, a care plan had to be put in place. I am grateful that my company gave me three months to work from Mom's house and get her settled before they made it clear I needed to go back on the road.

During those three months I was asking everyone I knew, even total strangers in the grocery store, "How did you handle this situation?" "What were the resources you found helpful?" "What lessons did you learn through this process?" It allowed Mom and me to understand that the best care plan for her meant finding a live-in caregiver. Through trial and error we concluded that we needed to hire a home care agency. Once that decision was made, it became an ongoing discussion about what Mom needed to feel comfortable.

There were three major requirements for hiring an aide:

♥ First, the aide could not be afraid of dogs. Our caregiver needed to be willing to let Bella out back where the yard is fenced in, and willing to feed her.

♥ Second, she needed to be able to drive so she could go grocery shopping weekly.

♥ Third, Mom needed to be able to understand her if English was not her first language.

My nonnegotiable during this process was that I wanted to interview the caregiver before hiring, and she had to be willing to have every other weekend off. Neither of these requirements were the norm when we were looking. After a home assessment an agency typically assigns a live-in to you and asks that you give it two to three weeks before asking for a new one. Normally, a live-in caregiver works four to five weeks before taking a weeks' vacation. I knew my mother would do better with a break that occurred more often. I knew with my travel schedule I would not be able to guarantee that I could be there during the caregiver's vacation week.

Have you ever gone through the interview process for a live-in? It's emotional and exhausting. We held a lot of interviews. During this process what my mother wanted and needed changed weekly. Sometimes my mother decided the person must drive a car, and sometimes it was OK if the person did not drive. This waffling back and forth was despite my telling her that we were limiting the candidate pool with the requirement to drive. Sometimes speaking English was less important than having someone she felt could be a companion. One day when I was working in her dining room and she was in the living room we once again started discussing an upcoming interview, and driving as a must was back on the table. Suddenly, a light bulb went off in my head. "Mom is playing me." And I was livid.

It's hard to rein in your emotions sometimes, isn't it? Looking back, I probably should have waited until I calmed down to set this boundary, but it didn't happen.

I looked at my mother and said, "I have got to go back to traveling in three weeks. We can't keep doing this. Every time we discuss a live-in, what you require changes. I'm done. You are a smart, intelligent woman who is perfectly capable of making these calls and these decisions. You will need to find and hire your own caregiver. I will help you find the agencies, make sure you have the phone numbers, anything you need. But as of right now, you're in charge of finding your live-in." And she did.

I know my mother wasn't deliberately trying to keep me from going back to my job. But in that moment it felt like it, and I jumped right into the conversation. I would handle it differently today, but I would still set that boundary. Hiring her own caregiver was scary for Mom. Up until then Dad or I had taken on these responsibilities. But in the end, taking control of the situation helped her feel more secure about the future and her ability to handle it.

Setting boundaries requires putting yourself first

There is a reason why a flight attendant tells you to put your oxygen mask on before helping someone else. As a people pleasing peacemaker, this is an important lesson—no matter how difficult it is to learn.

Setting boundaries is one of the most important aspects of your self-care. Without them, your time and energy, your very life, can get sucked out of you. Research has shown time and again the price caregivers pay when they are under constant stress and don't take care of their physical, mental, and emotional health. Setting boundaries is an important way to take care of yourself.

Do you feel like you have the right to draw a line in the sand and say, "this is not okay"? Saying "no" is not a reflection on how you feel about your loved one; it is about what you need. If you don't give yourself permission to put yourself first, you can feel disrespected and unsupported. When you do put yourself first, you can set clear boundaries. When you do put yourself first, you can offer an alternative or use the "No, but" technique.

When we hold back and don't draw that line in the sand, walls go up, a molehill can become a mountain, our feelings get hurt, and little issues become insurmountable. Maybe even more damaging for our loved ones is saying "yes," then not being able to live up to our promise.

If you feel like your schedule is running your life, then it's time to prioritize your relationships and activities. I did it for the first time this year. Instead of a New Year's resolution, I decided to focus on the word IMPACT, making it my touchstone through the year. I use this word to let go of commitments, activities, and people that don't have a positive impact in my life. There have been times over the last year when sitting across from someone or while I'm at an activity that in my head I'm thinking, "I don't have time for the people I love. What am I doing here?" That one thought has been the catalyst for change in much of my life.

As caregivers, so much of our lives are beyond our control. But I can still make thoughtful decisions on what to change and what to keep in my world. To borrow a phrase from Kathy Lee Gifford, "Honey, if you can't be a blessing, don't show up." When I don't feel like a blessing to a person or place, it is time to let it go.

Impact is my reminder to look at the things I am doing as Mom's caregiver, as a friend, as a professional, and measure the impact on my life. Is it serving me well? Does it bring me joy and satisfaction, or does it drain me? Too often as caregivers we are so busy that we forget or don't have (make) the time for this self-inventory. And really, isn't this where self-care starts?

Personal boundaries: What are we willing to do or not do for one another?

In this chapter we've been focused on emotional boundaries, but as we discussed in Chapter Two, many of us are called upon to take on physical tasks that can make us or our loved one uncomfortable.

First, this is a different type of boundary discussion. As previously mentioned, discussions that touch on helping our loved one with personal needs such as bathing or dressing require understanding and respecting one another's personal boundaries. Through conversation we can learn what help our loved one needs and how we can assist them in a way that is comfortable for both of us. The goal of a personal boundary conversation is to keep the other person's dignity intact and afford them as much privacy as possible. Clients tell me this is particularly challenging when you care for a parent of the opposite sex.

I suspect you will have more than one conversation about personal tasks during your caregiving journey. What might start out as cutting hair will over time most likely move to more intimate tasks such as help with incontinence. Because we are always co-creating our relationship contract, we have a way to ensure we are on top of personal boundary changes. Ongoing work on our relationship contract gives us a way to ensure that we continue to respect our loved one's personal boundaries. And it allows for new personal boundaries as a caregiver. If a new task takes us out of our comfort level, we can hire someone to help.

In addition to personal care boundaries, there are often privacy boundaries around information such as finances. Banks, insurance, and investment firms will require written documentation that you have the legal right to pay bills, make financial decisions, or even talk to them. The effects of not having legal documents in place can be devastating and long-lasting. Even after her father moved in, my friend Anna found this to be one of the single most difficult conversations to have with him. It took months to get his permission for her to be his Durable Power of Attorney (POA) for finances.

These interactions can be difficult and scary conversations for everyone involved. Our loved ones are faced with giving up things they have always done for themselves. We need to understand that there is grief in this letting go—for them and for us. They grieve independence and letting go of the life they've lived for years, and we grieve as we come to terms with our parent's frailty.

Exercise Ten
Destructive Patterns

Find a quiet space to think about the past week. To get started, pull out your schedule. Look over everything you had to take care of for your family, caree, work, school, etc. Where in your schedule did you feel angry, resentful, or exhausted? Write down:

- ♥ The emotion
- ♥ Who's need did you feel obligated to meet
- ♥ What you were being asked to do
- ♥ Your "yes" or "no" response to the request

When you say "yes," what patterns do you see appear? Does the pressure to meet other people's needs happen more often at home, work, with people you know, or strangers?

Exercise Eleven
Determine What Needs to Change

If your schedule is running your life and a major stressor, then it's time to prioritize your relationships and activities.

To prioritize relationships and activities, it requires a change in mindset. Change begins with recognizing that you have the right to say "no" and not feel guilty. Once you give yourself permission to put yourself first, a "no" with no apologies or using the 'No, but' technique becomes easier.

Using your destructive patterns worksheet:
- ♥ List relationships from highest to lowest priority.
- ♥ List activities from highest to lowest priorities.

Then decide:
- ♥ Which of these relationships can you invest less time in?
- ♥ Which activities can you delegate or get help on?
- ♥ Which of these activities can you do less often or let go of completely?

Before moving on, look at the list of people and activities. If it doesn't include people who support you without question or things that nourish your soul, go back and add them.

Exercise Twelve
Practice Moving from "Yes" to "No"

Looking at your patterns, how often do you say "yes" when the right answer is "no"?

Saying "no" takes practice. It is easier to develop this skill with people in whom you don't have a high emotional investment. Use the list of low priority relationships and activities for practice.

Three techniques to practice:
1. The easiest technique is to buy yourself time and space to say "no." You are not obligated to say anything in that moment. Instead say: "Let me get back to you." or "I'll think about it and get back to you."
2. "No, but" takes a bit more practice. This technique works beautifully if you have no intention of fulfilling a request. It lets you offer an alternative. "I can't help you but let me put you in touch with someone who may be able to help."

   "No, but" is often at the end of an internal conversation and quick self-reflection: "Is this something I must do, or can it be done by someone else?" "Does it have to be done this very minute or can it be done another time?"

3. "No" is a complete statement. You may want to soften your answer with "No, I can't." When you use this technique, it doesn't need to sound confrontational or as if you are judging the request. You don't need to apologize or make excuses for your feelings and needs.

Once your patterns become clear, recognition hits quickly so you can employ the techniques you've practiced in that moment. Over time you will find your own ways to say "no" that can be educational or inspiring to the other person.

Exercise Thirteen
"Yes" to "No" Worksheets

1. Stressors
Activity(ies): Bake cupcakes for end of year picnic Person(s) involved: My child's classroom mother Emotion: Resentment Response: (Yes) or No

2. List relationships and prioritize
    1. Husband
    2. Children
    3. Mom
    4. Boss
    5. ??
 	
I can invest less time in:
My son's classroom mother
My co-worker

3. List activities and prioritize
    1. Dinner
    2. Homework
    3. Mom to doctor
    4. Book club
    5. Line dancing
    6. Grocery shopping
    7. Baking for school
 	
I can get help with:
Grocery shopping—ask husband to order online and pick up once a week.
 	
I can change or let go of:
Baking for school—buy cupcakes from the grocery store.

4. "No" technique to put into place When asked to bake for a school event: "No, I won't be able to bake but I'd be happy to pick up a dozen of baked goods from the local bakery and drop them off the night before."

Chapter 6
Ask for and Say "YES" to Help

"Boundaries are the flip side of asking for help. And if you can do both... if you can learn to say 'no' and 'I need your help,' you might just survive this experience."

Anne Tumlinson, Daughterhood.org

Dad's hospitalization was the first time I realized how critical it was for me to say "yes" to each offer of help and to ask for help. At the same time, I realized how hard it is for my parents' generation to do the same. I'm not sure why this is true. I suspect it is a combination of not wanting to lose their independence, burying their heads in the sand about health and/or privacy concerns. This is particularly difficult for a generation that grew up not airing "dirty laundry." No matter the reason, clients tell me it is a struggle to get their loved ones to accept help, whether it is from family members or professionals.

You know from the previous chapter on boundaries that the two weeks Dad was in the hospital were chaotic and exhausting. I was drowning, and Mom didn't know it because I wasn't telling anyone how overwhelmed I was feeling. The truth is, I didn't even realize it. I was on autopilot, just trying to meet everyone's needs. About a week into Dad's two-week stay in the hospital this happened.

I had just come back to Mom's after my morning hospital visit. I sat down to work when my aunt called. I wasn't paying attention to the conversation until I heard my mother say, "No, we don't need any help." Suddenly, something clicked, and my head shot up like an explosion had gone off. I said, "Mom, wait a minute. Let me talk to Aunt Pat."

Honestly, I had to stop myself from ripping the phone out of her hands.

In that conversation I made it clear that we did need help. Because of Mom's mobility issues, bringing her to see Dad every day was simply not practical. But Mom sitting at home worried and isolated while I was at the hospital was not healthy. I constantly felt torn and guilty because I had no energy to devote to her, other than caregiving tasks. If Aunt Pat would coordinate extended family members visiting Dad, it meant I could spend less time at the hospital, freeing me up to do everything else. Or if family members could keep Mom company while I was with Dad, I would be less stressed and feel less guilty.

When I got off the phone Mom and I started talking about ways in which we could ask for and say "yes" to help when it was offered. It was the first of several conversations, and it was a sea change for both of us.

During our conversations about the help we needed, I was able to remind her that one of the reasons we were keeping her at home was that there was a support system within her neighborhood and from nearby family. For years she had reached out and helped others. Allowing these same people to help her gave them a chance to "pay it back." A relationship has to feel equal; people are uncomfortable when it's not. I reminded her that people can always say "no." And I reminded her that despite having a live-in, there were things that person could not do. For example, a live-in from an agency is not allowed to get on ladders. If a light in the kitchen ceiling blew out, it didn't make sense for her to wait until I came up to change it. Nor was I going to drive 50 minutes to immediately change a light bulb when a simple phone call to her next-door neighbor could solve the problem.

One of the barriers to seniors accepting this kind of help is the awkward "let me pay you" conversation that often comes up. I understand how pride and the independence needs of our loved one may be in jeopardy when the person doing them the favor refuses payment. My beloved Aunt Mary Ellen, who we lost to lung cancer, had this practical and helpful suggestion. Buy gift cards from your local grocery store, or any store you frequent, and give them to the folks who offer to pick up what you need. This trick eliminates the awkward "let me pay you" conversation and the times you don't have cash on hand. When you know they are nearing the end of the gift card's usefulness, give them another one.

How to say YES to help

There are several things you and your caree can do to make it easier to accept the help that is offered.

♥ Be ready with a list.

When people ask "what can I do to help?" take advantage of their generosity and be ready with a list of specific and time-bound tasks you can reference. A clearly outlined request, with time and frequency noted, is more likely to be fulfilled than a vague "can you walk the dog?" Otherwise the person may say "yes" to something that, in reality, they are not able to do for you. Asking "Can you walk the dog Monday and Wednesday afternoon between three and five o'clock?" sets clear expectations. It gives the person offering help the opportunity to make sure the time and frequency works with their schedule, while leaving both of you room to negotiate a new plan.

In a crisis, making this list may seem insurmountable. If you take the time to create the task list discussed in Chapter One, you already have most of what you need.

♥ Play to people's strengths.

If the bathroom toilet seems to be running incessantly, don't ask someone that has no plumbing experience over to take a look and give you an opinion. By the same token, don't expect the person with some knowledge to fix the toilet. It's one thing to have your suspicion confirmed, and another to ask the person to go to Home Depot, pick up a part, and replace it for you. I know people with expectations that go way beyond other people's boundaries.

There are times I've even called Mom's young neighbor for help. I had to replace the battery in a large box that brings the internet into the house. I could not get the cover off. Sometimes it just takes brute strength, and then I can take it from there.

♥ Play to people's comfort levels.

When Dad was in the hospital, I asked my cousin if she would visit him over the lunch hour. I was so thankful for her honesty when she shared doing hospital visits was difficult for her. Without her willingness to brave the truth, she might have said "yes," then never offered help again because this request made her uncomfortable. "No problem! Can you come stay with Mom, visit with her, and help her cook or clean out the junk drawer while I go to the hospital?" When you have a list, you can move onto the next item if the first suggestion is out of the person's comfort level or not one of their strengths.

Reserve the right to come back to them

There were times when someone would call and ask if they could do anything to help. If there was nothing on my list or it was not the right task for them, I would use the "No, but" strategy. "Right now I am good but I am going to reserve the right to come back to you when there is something you can do to help." Not one person turned me down when I went back and asked for help.

We found in an emergency people are wonderful. They are sincere in their offers of help. They just don't know what they can do to help, which is why being prepared with your list can make all the difference in the world. Take advantage of each and every offer because, realistically, after the emergency offers of help will slow down and even stop. It's not that folks don't care, but everyone is busy. Expecting friends and family to keep up the same level of support once an emergency has passed isn't realistic. This is where the habit of asking for help can be a lifesaver.

Why a loved one may refuse help

We already talked about some of the potential reasons our loved ones will refuse help: loss of independence, not being realistic about their own health problems, or not wanting anyone to know they need help. I'm going to offer you another possible reason: the difficulty of coping with life as health and mobility declines.

I noticed that as my parents aged and their health declined, their ability to cope with the smallest household problem or change in routine declined as well. I came to realize that life was overwhelming for them. My father was so focused on managing his congestive heart failure that everything else was beyond him. When Dad died, Mom was not used to dealing with household problems and had no idea where to start.

If you realize this is true of your loved one as well, then understand that asking for help or finding resources for help may be something they don't have the time or energy to do.

This is where you can help as the caregiver. Ask the question "What do you want me to do?" Then:

♥ Offer to do the research for places and people that can help.

♥ Offer alternatives that keep in mind this is still their house and their life—and make a decision as a family.

♥ Give your opinion only when it is asked for.

The bottom line is to act as your parents' partner, not their parent, when it comes to their lifestyle and household decisions. A partnership continues to give them control of their lives, which is important to them and I hope important to you.

When a loved one refuses help

Saying "no" to help, or refusing to even entertain the idea of getting help, is probably the single most frustrating thing our loved one can do. It's bad enough when they won't accept the help of a professional such as a home healthcare aide. But when they won't accept help from us, their caregivers, it is a disaster waiting to happen. At least it certainly feels that way to us. Unfortunately, this is another situation where your loved one has the right to make the wrong decision.

Here are strategies you can use to try and get them to say "yes" to help from you or anyone else.

As with all hard conversations, carefully pick the time and place to have the discussion. And when you bring up the subject:

♥ Don't start the conversation in such a way that the other person feels attacked. Derogatory comments on their lifestyle or decisions will not get you far. Words and tone of voice matter.

♥ Use language that keeps the control with your senior while offering choices. Use language that validates their feelings and concerns.

♥ Understand what their boundaries are and work with them. If the thought of someone living with them pushes a boundary, then you're better off suggesting some help coming in a couple hours a week. You can always increase the time later. The goal is to get to "yes."

♥ Don't expect the conversation to be one and done. The Drip Method really can work. After age 70 your senior is constantly processing their life and their legacy. Even if they don't admit it, they know when they need help. Give them enough time to examine their life; suddenly, when the fourth time you gently bring up the subject, "no" becomes a "yes."

♥ Since you have been quietly assessing their Activities of Daily Living (ADLs) and Instrumental Activities of Daily Living (IADLs), you are aware of when help or a change to your caregiving routine is on the horizon. When you know what options are available, you are armed for a discussion on help.

♥ In the conversation, don't list the things they can no longer do without help. Instead, highlight everything that they will be able to do with help—especially if it is something they love to do and they have had to put it aside.

♥ Ask peers of your senior or a voice of authority such as a physician to intervene. Often hearing the exact same thing from someone that is not a child resonates differently. Suddenly, your loved one is willing to entertain the solution you have been advocating.

For Mom and me, one of the most difficult "yeses" was saying "yes" to live-in care for her. As children of adults who need caregiving, we can feel disloyal and guilty if we are not the ones giving 24/7 hands-on care. But not everyone is able to be their loved one's primary caregiver. You may need to continue working full time, you may live out of state, and sometimes you just can't to it. All of these and more are perfectly valid reasons for not taking on the role of a live-in caregiver—all the more reason to ask for and say "yes" to help.

When you offer help

When (not if) you are in the position to offer help, please, I beg of you, don't say, "Call me if you need anything." When I was in crisis mode with Dad, I could not come up for air, let alone think clearly enough to call someone and ask for help. For me, that is a non-offer of help that puts an additional burden on the caregiver. What I would have appreciated was a call like this: "I'm going to the grocery store. Is there anything you need?" Any concrete suggestion or offer would have allowed me to clear the fog out of my head and answer the question. This is without a doubt one of my biggest caregiver hot buttons.

Caregivers need to ask for and say "yes" to help as well

Sometimes the shoe is on the other foot. We caregivers can be reluctant to ask for and say "yes" to help just like our parents. Personally, I could not have gotten through Dad's hospitalizations without the help of family and friends. The sense of relief, of feeling I was not alone, of feeling loved by the supportive offers of help, carries over into these last years as Mom's caregiver. Do we need today the level or type of help we needed when Dad was dying? No, but that experience proved to me how important asking for and saying "yes" to help is to my mental and physical well-being. No one person is ever meant to do this alone.

The well documented statistics on the toll caregiving can take on you is one reason you are not meant to be a caregiving "Lone Ranger." Here are a few:

Family caregivers experiencing extreme stress have been shown to age prematurely. This level of stress can take as much as 10 years off a family caregiver's life.

Elissa S. Epel, Dept. of Psychiatry
Univ. of Calif., San Francisco, et al.
From the Proceedings of the National Academy of Sciences,
Dec. 7, 2004, Vol. 101, No. 49

Nearly three quarters (72%) of family caregivers report not going to the doctor as often as they should, and 55% say they skip doctor appointments for themselves. 63% of caregivers report having poorer eating habits than noncaregivers, and 58% indicate worse exercise habits than before caregiving responsibilities.

"Evercare Study of Caregivers in Decline: A Close-Up Look at
Health Risks of Caring for a Loved One"
National Alliance for Caregiving and Evercare, 2006.

20% of employed female caregivers over 50 years old report symptoms of depression compared to 8% of their noncaregiving peers.

"MetLife Study of Working Caregivers and Employer
Health Costs"
National Alliance for Caregiving and MetLife
Mature Market Institute, February 2010

Given the statistics, is it any wonder that one of the most written about caregiver topics is self-care? From my perspective, getting help as a caregiver is a huge part of my self-care. Not only does asking for and saying "yes" to help alleviate stress, it helps ease feelings of isolation and loneliness for me and Mom.

It is time to get help if you are:
♥ Feeling tired, overwhelmed, sad, depressed, anxious, or constantly worried
♥ Gaining or losing weight
♥ Easily irritated or angry
♥ Getting frequent bodily pain or headaches
♥ Losing interest in activities and social events you used to enjoy

Why do caregivers resist saying "yes" to help?

The reasons are as varied as individual caregivers, often take root in family values and norms, or may reflect the relationship between caregiver and caree. Which of these common barriers to help are yours? Are there several?
♥ We want/need to be the person who provides the care. We don't believe anyone else can keep our loved one as safe and healthy as we can. Pride and reluctance to give up control are detrimental to your health if they stop you from getting help.
♥ We feel guilty if we are not the one "doing" for our loved one. After all, we are the spouse, adult child, or parent of the one in need. Don't feel that asking for help is a sign of weakness or worry that you will be judged by family and friends.
♥ Our place in the family (oldest/youngest/closest proximity) or even sibling rivalry requires us to be the primary caregiver. This is especially true if we have an overdeveloped sense of responsibility.
♥ We don't trust hired caregivers—strangers to care for our loved one. We fear what can happen if we can't protect them ourselves. Or we might get frustrated when someone approaches a caregiving task differently than we would.

Privacy is a strong and cherished family value. We consider opening our home, family, and sensitive information to strangers or even people we know like neighbors to be intolerable.

How can caregivers get beyond saying "no" and say "yes" to help?

♥ If you are resistant to help in all forms, you may need to seek guidance from a person outside the family such as a clergy member. Someone outside the family can often see destructive familial patterns that we cannot. Hearing that we are not expected to carry the full load of caregiving alone from an impartial third party is often easier. After all, they have no hidden agenda.

♥ Talk to other caregivers. No one understands what you are going through like another person in the middle of the caregiving tornado (see the Resource section for resources on caregiving support).

♥ Don't believe all the bad news you hear about professional caregivers. There are many good and caring agencies that hire terrific people with training that can help either part time or full time.

♥ If finances are holding you back, talk to an elder law attorney, an aging life care specialist, or another professional such as a Certified Caregiving Consultant™. They will educate you and steer you to financial help you may not know is available.

Some ways to organize your help network

Once you have the list of tasks people can help you with and the list of helpers, there are several ways to organize and mobilize your team. In those first couple of months after Dad died, there was so much I didn't know about my new caregiver role. One of the ways people were able to help was to research a question and send me links to pertinent articles. Once they got me started, I was able to take it from there and find the answers.

I found that a closed Facebook group of family and friends who had offered help to be invaluable. Limiting each post to one specific item meant that everyone in the group saw it so we were not mixing requests. When someone could fulfill the task, everyone knew it was taken care of because there was an "I've got this" comment on the post.

If you are completely overwhelmed and can't monitor this type of notice board, ask a trusted friend to monitor it and keep you posted. When I needed one person to take care of a request, I could Instant Message (IM) that person for an individual ask. A group text is another good way to ask for help on an individual task.

In these five years as a caregiver, one of the most important lessons is how my quality of life and Mom's has improved by our willingness to ask for and say "yes" to help.

Exercise Fourteen
Strategies to Say "Yes" to Help: Create a Help List

Write down everything you can think of that would help in specific terms. Include things that can be done for your caree, you, and other people in your life such as your children.

Model each request for help after the SMART objectives mnemonic. Every ask for help should be:

Specific: Walk the dog on Tuesdays and Thursdays.

Measurable: Dog is calm when you get back late from the hospital.

Achievable: Their schedule permits these days and times.

Relevant: The dog is used to being walked when you get home from work.

Time-bound: between 5:00 and 7:00 p.m.

"Can you walk the dog Tuesday and Thursday evenings between 5:00 and 7:00 p.m.?"

With an ask for help that is SMART, you can modify the time or day.

For each help request you list, add all the people who you think would be good at a task and who would be comfortable with the task. Now when someone asks if they can help, you have a list you can run down. Don't forget: If you don't need help right then, reserve the right to come back to them later.

If you need to ask for help, you can start with your "go-to" list of people. Contact can be by phone, by text, or, to be really efficient, via a private social media forum such as a closed Facebook group.

Don't wait to ask for or say "yes" to help. It is past time to create these lists if you are showing any of these burnout symptoms:

♥ Feeling tired, overwhelmed, sad, depressed, anxious, or constantly worried
♥ Gaining or losing weight
♥ Easily irritated or angry
♥ Getting frequent bodily pain or headaches
♥ Losing interest in activities and social events you used to enjoy

Chapter 7
Your Caregiving Support Peeps

"The thing about old friends is not that they love you but that they know you."
Anna Quindlen, author of "Lots of Candles, Plenty of Cake"

In previous chapters we talked about the importance of setting boundaries as well as asking for and saying "yes" to help. Both skills are fundamental to creating time and space for yourself. The most critical boundary to set is the one that carves out desperately needed respite.

When you give in and acknowledge you can't do this job alone, reaching out to your support network for self-care time becomes easier. The importance of your support network in maintaining your mental and physical well-being can't be overstated.

The "me" time you create with boundaries, and your support network can be time for an activity or person you love. It's your time and should be whatever you need to rejuvenate, even if it is simply a nap. For many caregivers, this boundary may be the hardest of all to set. It means taking time away from your caree, and that can make us feel guilty and selfish. If you believe you are the only one who can care for your loved one properly, then it becomes an issue about giving up control.

Self-care combats isolation

"Isolation and exhaustion are head-on the two biggest issues for caregivers. If not addressed, disease and depression are often the result." Elissia Lewin, Founder of Nancy's House

The truth is, caregiving can be an incredibly isolating experience. During a crisis or in the midst of everyday exhaustion, it can feel overwhelming to reach out to family, friends, your faith community, or eldercare professionals. I know I've felt this way, and by nature I'm an extrovert. If you're an introvert, reaching out can feel beyond your energy level. As hard as it is, especially if you are an introvert, find a way even once a week to reach out. If you don't, if you self-isolate, there is an increased risk of isolation and depression.

My support network

I don't know if it is because I am back living in the state I grew up in, or if it is because I come from a large Irish and Italian extended family, but I am very blessed, and I know it. Moving back to New Jersey means I have family as well as childhood and adulthood friends that are part of my caregiver support network. I call them my caregiver "peeps."

My caregiver peeps share history with my mom and me. They know us, love us, and can be honest with us. Because we share history, they often know what I need even before I do. Even so, it takes work to maintain these relationships. When I am overwhelmed or exhausted, I don't want to reach out. But I've learned this is when I need my support system the most. So even if I reach out with just a quick text, a "hey, how are you?" I then feel connected and less isolated.

As humans we need to be able to express our thoughts and feelings in a space that feels safe. A support network gives us that space. And it can allow relationships we've had for years to deepen and grow, which carries us through the hard times.

Recently my best friend and I committed to talking once a week. This phone call is more than just catching up with one another, although we do that as well. We committed to share during this call the best and worst of what happened that week.

Now we've known each other for more than 40 years and have seen each other through good times and bad. But this sharing is different. It has given us the opportunity to be open and vulnerable with one another in a way that a laundry list of what we did since the last time we talked never allowed. Because it requires introspection and reflection, patterns start to emerge. Sometimes I see them, and sometimes she does.

I'm surprised at the things I'm learning about her even after 40 years of friendship, and I know she feels the same. I've been surprised by how often our emotions and feelings mirror one another, even though the situations that bring them up differ. Think about someone in your life who would be willing to start this practice with you. It may just make all the difference in the world.

Your support network

The risk of isolation is real. Early in your caregiving journey, during that time when your "spidey" sense kicks in and you start to think "uh oh, something is going on," is the perfect time to start to identify your support network, especially if you don't have family and friends you've known for years as I did. The struggle to identify your support network is real because the way we live in community is drastically different than our parents and grandparents. This is why it is so important not to bury your head in the sand. It makes a huge difference when a support network is in place before a crisis, before the tornado of caregiving sweeps you up and life feels out of control.

Your support network, or "your caregiver peeps" list, is different than the list of people that support your senior, although it may have some of the same people on it. This is the list of people you can turn to in times of crisis, when you need to talk, and when you need physical help. It may contain dear friends or family, acquaintances from faith community, or professionals in the caregiving field. It may contain people you've never met but talk to consistently in an online caregiver support group.

What your support network gives you, and what you need from them, is as varied as the people on your list. Some of these folks may run errands or sit with your loved one while you take a break. Others will let you vent without judgment. Someone else may be a fountain of resources because he or she has more years of experience in caregiving. If you're not sure what you need, imagine someone standing next to you right now. What would you ask of that person? Do you need to talk, to have company at dinner, a hug? Whatever role the person plays in your life, having them and reaching out to them IS self-care. So find the small pockets of time, despite how hard it is to take that time, and connect with your caregiver peeps.

Because families are smaller than years past, and as a society we are more mobile and may no longer live where we grew up, many caregivers don't have an easily identifiable support network. If this is your world, where you don't have family or ties to the community, one place to start looking for help is with community resources such as the Area Agency on Aging. This is a federal program found in your county or city that has professionals on staff familiar with local senior services and programming. Because these offices are based locally, they are tapped into nonprofit and faith-based groups that can offer help and respite along with federal, state, and local resources.

The National Council on Aging has a BenefitsCheckUp tool to prescreen your loved one and you for benefit eligibility. Some of the benefits provided are: Family Caregiver Support and Respite Care, transportation, and help with chores, along with the more traditional Meals on Wheels.

If these resources cover the physical and financial help you need, but not the emotional, don't give up. There are caregiver support groups run by local hospitals, eldercare facilities such as assisted living, and groups such as the Alzheimer's Association. If you can't make these physical meetings or you're wide awake at 2 a.m., there are amazing online support networks available to you. I have the pleasure of participating in several online groups and am always amazed by the support and care the participants show one another. There is often a level of intimacy in the sharing of good times and bad that can occur when you are not face to face.

Online resources run the gamut from health communities such as SmartPatient.com to caregiver specific communities such as Caregiving.com and closed Facebook groups including the Caregivers Hub Support Group, Caring for Elderly Parents, and Exhale First, to name a few. To find local Facebook caregiver support groups, use the platform's search feature. If you are unfamiliar with Facebook groups, a closed group usually asks you to answer a few questions about your circumstances before approving you to be part of the group.

A support system, whether it is in-person or online, helps us to deal with adverse situations and feelings. A support system helps with our resilience now and after our role as a caregiver ends. If you are lucky enough to have a support system, take care of those relationships. Don't let every conversation be about you and your situation. Be sure to be involved in the lives of your supporters by helping and supporting them as well.

I've said this earlier, but it bears repeating. Don't wait to identify your support network, especially if family or friends live far away or are limited in number. If you wait too long to reach out, you may be so exhausted it is beyond your energy level. If you wait too long to reach out, an attitude of "no one will help us" can prevent you from seeing opportunities where help is possible. If you wait too long you run the risk of becoming an energy vampire—the person whose negativity sucks the life out of the group.

When you're not willing to try solutions offered, it won't be long before people stop offering you help. There are times when I know I'm the energy vampire, times when it feels like all I do is complain.

You know what? It's okay to complain—for a little while. But no one, least of all me, wants to hear about the same problem over and over again. I've come to realize the third time I hear myself whine about the same issue it's time to say, "Enough, do something about this. Change the way you deal with it, or your attitude, and stop complaining about it." Sometimes it is difficult to follow your own advice, isn't it?

Family of origin vs. family of choice

"We're forced to create our tribes during seasons of our life when we have the least time and energy to do so."

Writer and life coach Beth Berry

A wise friend once said to me, "We all have a family of origin and a family of choice. Your family of origin may be unable to give you what you need because of distance, both physical and emotional. Your family of choice are the people you bring into your life, your tribe, that supports, loves, and nourishes you, and you do the same for them."

This made perfect sense to me from the moment I heard it. While in graduate school I had the privilege of interning in the public policy office of the American Home Economics Association, now known as the American Association of Family and Consumer Sciences (AAFCS). During my tenure I was tasked with writing the association's position paper on a bill known as "The Family Protection Act" introduced by Orrin Hatch in the late 1970s. In that bill were 38 provisions that among other things narrowly defined the family and impacted federal program funding.

At that time, AAFCS had one of the most forward-thinking and inclusive definitions of family. This bill was direct opposite of the association's definition:

"Family is defined as a unit of intimate, transacting, and interdependent persons who share some values and goals, resources, responsibility for decisions, and have commitment to one another over time."

Nowhere did it state that family must be related by blood or be within the confines of a marriage. That definition of family, along with my education as a home economist and my work in public policy, continues to shape how I view families.

My family of origin is large and close-knit. As kids, we went to visit both sets of grandparents every Sunday and most holidays. The bond I formed with my cousins during childhood is unbreakable. But now as adults, we rarely get together. Many are married with children and grandchildren; everyone is busy with their lives. I am painfully aware, as I watch my mother's world grow smaller, that my family of origin and my family of choice are growing older. As time goes on, my support network will get smaller and smaller if I don't work to grow it now.

How DO you create a family of choice?

Start with determining your own needs, be ready to step outside of your comfort zone, and be open to family in all its forms.

A great place to start is getting to know your neighbors. We homeowners tend to scurry from our cars to our house, often through the garage, so meeting people is difficult. Taking the time to say hello, commenting on a garden, or engaging a young child while out in the neighborhood are icebreakers that have worked for me. The easiest way I've meet neighbors is while walking my dog. For ages since I moved into my house I only knew people as "Ginger's mom" or "Boomer's dad," but we forged a bond that continues today. After we got to know one another a bit I started hosting a watch party for a favorite TV show with several female neighbors.

We called it our B and B night: No boys, No bras.

The first time I moved out of state it was very lonely. I'd moved to Pennsylvania for my first job and knew no one. Oddly enough, not knowing one another was the topic of conversation every time I would meet someone getting mail or in the parking lot. Instead of commiserating with one another, a small group of us decided to organize a potluck picnic. We left flyers with the date and time on apartment doors. We invited people to bring lawn chairs and food to share at a big open space between the two apartment buildings. Someone brought out a boom box, someone else a badminton set. I brought my bocce ball set. It was a blast, and friendships were formed that lasted all the years I lived in Pennsylvania, even when I moved to another town. Today I'm more likely to invite neighbors over for a drink or coffee, but the idea is still the same.

If you're not up to organizing a social event, consider spearheading a group that creates a list of names, phone numbers, and skills for everyone living in the neighborhood. To be included on the list, you must commit to helping one another, and being helped.

A tried and true way to meet like-minded people is through volunteering. You may find that people who volunteer are by nature more open when you ask them for help and are more open to accepting help.

Faith communities are a great place to get your feet wet as a volunteer. The advantage in having a faith community and being involved is the natural support networks built into them. As with any other organization, you get what you give. When people see you offering time and help to others, they are more likely willing to step in and help you when you have a need.

Even if you're not a big faith community person, these institutions often offer educational programs or serve as places where support groups and community organizations meet. You may go for a support group, and leave with a new friend or mentor, or be able to help someone else through an extremely difficult time.

Become a part of something you love. Meetup is an online platform used to find and build local communities. It is a great place to find people with the same interests you have or to try something new that will take you out of your comfort zone. Another place to find people with similar interests is through groups on Facebook.

Making close friends is hard as we get older. Keeping close

friends is hard when we are steeped in caregiving. There is that old saying: "To get a friend, be a friend." That means keep your caregiver peeps close. Make the effort to stay in contact. Get together as often as possible. At least once a month, schedule time to be with someone on your list in person or by phone. Families are built and strengthened with regular connection.

Don't let your identity get swallowed up by caregiving

One of the fallouts of caregiving is that we can lose our identity. I understood on some level that this happens, but it wasn't until I heard myself say for the umpteenth time: "Mom is good so I'm good." Wait, what? When did this become my standard reply to the question, "How are you?"

When I realized how often I gave this answer it scared me. What did this response say about my mental, emotional, and physical health? What did "Mom is good so I'm good" say about being in touch with who I was as Deb, not as Doris's caregiver? I get that my life is less stressful when Mom is healthy and doing well, but this way of measuring my well-being against something I can't control is crazy.

What about when someone asks, "What's new?" Is your response all about caregiving? If you must think about what's new outside of your role as a caregiver, it's time to reevaluate, figure out where you lost your identity, and how to get it back. If you're thinking "I don't have TIME for that!" you need it more than you know. This is when having even one person in your support network who knows you, who helped shape your place in the world, can help. Taking a break from caregiving to spend time with this person, even if it is over the phone or online, reconnects you with the essence of who you are beyond a caregiver.

Another way to reconnect with who you are is to think about what you loved to do as a child. What activities did you do alone or in a group that gave you joy?

At one point in my career I was deeply unhappy in my work. I worked with a coach who gave me exercises, some mental, some requiring drawing or writing. The goal of all these exercises was to get me thinking about what gives me joy, makes me feel fulfilled, and makes me feel good about myself and my place in the world. It was a great exercise to go through. I am never going to be a professional dancer, but the joy I got from dancing made it well worth my while to take Zumba and line dancing classes. Reconnecting with something I loved to do made even the parts of my work I disliked easier to bear.

What brings you joy? Have you let it go? Are there ways you can bring bits and pieces of these joy-filled things back into your life? It often means asking for help—and that's a good thing.

Self-care

"Self-care isn't a one-time action. It's also not going to cause a complete turnaround of your condition overnight. It's a lifestyle choice, one where you have to commit yourself and practice daily."
"The Caregiver Space: Self-Care for Caregivers: Your Burden Matters" by Guest Author

Because I live near family and friends I have known for years that much of my self-care is finding and making time to be with them. To relax, laugh, have a meal together, see a movie—activities that we shared before I took on this role—remind me I am more than Mom's caregiver. Journaling, using music as a relaxation technique, and a monthly massage are also part of my self-care routine.

Self-care is different for everyone. It might take the form of exercise, eating healthy, time in the garden, building something that lets you pound out your frustration, or going to the movies. As long as what you are doing (or not doing) is something that brings you joy, makes you laugh, allows you to sit quietly and clear your mind, then it is self-care. Self-care brings you back to YOU, which allows you to keep parts of your life before you became a caregiver.

One of the ways I hope you will conduct self-care is through touch. When you see friends, give them a heart-to-heart hug. Hugs with your face to the right of the other person hugging for two deep breaths, build connections and deepen relationships. Don't discount the value of a massage. Never mind the healthy benefits of getting your lymph nodes moving or relieving pain; touch is critical to humans.

The term "failure to thrive" is used to describe babies who are not held, nuzzled, or hugged enough. Without those vital touches, they stop growing. I think as caregivers if we are not careful, we can fail to thrive as well.

Compassion fatigue

"Caring too much can hurt. When caregivers focus on others without practicing self-care, destructive behaviors can surface. Apathy, isolation, bottled up emotions, and substance abuse head a long list of symptoms associated with the secondary traumatic stress disorder now labeled: Compassion Fatigue."

The Compassion Fatigue Awareness Project©

Compassion fatigue is real. Dr. Eric Gentry, a leading traumatologist, suggests that it is common among people working in other-directed caregiving. Initially, I thought it was found only in professions such as nursing. But the proliferation of family caregivers has shown that we can suffer from compassion fatigue as well. Symptoms are the normal displays of chronic stress. The folks most likely to suffer from it learned at an early age to put everyone else's needs before theirs. To avoid compassion fatigue, family caregivers, like others working in direct care, need authentic, ongoing care practices.

If you needed a reason to practice self-care, to make the time to be with friends, relax, do something you love that you gave up, avoiding compassion fatigue is the one.

Caregiving is hard. If you're not careful, it can destroy the relationship you have with your caree and other family members. If you're not careful, chronic stress will result in compassion fatigue. Support from your peeps (in-person or online) can help you get beyond the overwhelming tasks, the business of caregiving, and relieve stress. And the most important benefit? You reclaim who you are as a whole person, not just a caregiver.

Exercise Fifteen
Strategies for Caregiver Support

Write down what you need to feel supported in your caregiving role. If you don't know where to start, imagine standing next to someone. What would you ask of that person?

- ♥ A friendly voice when it's been a rough day?
- ♥ A sounding board to make sure you are making the right medical decision?
- ♥ A movie or dinner companion?

♥   Someone who could come stay with your loved one while you napped, went shopping, or to the doctor?

Write down a list of family and friends that can serve as your support peeps. Include people from your family of origin and your family of choice. It doesn't matter if they live near or far, or if it has been years since you have been in contact.

Add to the list community resources such as the local office of the Area Agency on Aging, caregiver support groups run by organizations such as your local hospital, an assisted living facility, or a group such as one that provides support for living with Alzheimer's.

Include online resources such as closed Facebook groups, Twitter chats, and health communities such as SmartPatients.com

If you don't know of any community resources:

♥   Start with an office of the Area Agency on Aging. There is one found in every state at the regional and local levels; they exist to address the needs and concerns of all older persons.

♥   Look up national organizations that are specific to your loved one's diagnosis to see if they offer caregiver support either online or in local meetings.

♥   Search on Facebook for caregiver support groups. You will find both general groups and ones specific to your caregiving situation such as "caring for elderly parents." Only participate in closed groups.

Compare the list of what you need to feel supported to the list of caregiver peeps. Who can you reach out to for a movie night? What organization or online resources do you trust for advice? Once you have reconnected, stay in contact at least once a month—in person, by phone, or online.

Self-care strategies

Make a list of the activities you loved to do as child. Is there one you can incorporate into your life now as an adult?

♥   Make a list of everything that can help you relax.

♥   Make a list of everything that nourishes your body.

♥   Make a list of everything that nourishes your soul.

♥   Make a list of things that will improve your life.

Exercise Sixteen
Strategies for Caregiver Support

1. What makes me feel supported as a caregiver and in my noncaregiving role?

- Someone to bounce decisions off
   - Someone to go out to dinner or the movies
   - Someone to call and talk about anything but caregiving

2a. Family and friends
1. Kathleen
2. Chuck
3. Denise

2b. Community resources
1. Interfaith Caregivers
2. Caring for Aging Parents – Facebook closed group
3. Caregiving.com
4. Caregiver Volunteers of Central Jersey

2c. Caregiver peeps
1. Kathleen: monthly lunches
2. Chuck: help sorting out medical information
3. Denise: weekly phone call

3. Self-care strategies
What relaxes me?
1. Weightless by Marconi Union for music meditation
2. Write down what is worrying me just before I get in bed
3. Massage

What nourishes my body?
1. Walk the dog
2. Take a bath
3. Eating healthy

What nourishes my soul?
1. Working in the garden
2. Reading
3. Taking a ride in the country

What can I do right now to improve my life?
1. Set up online bill paying for Mom
2. Call the plumber to fix the toilet
3. Replace all the burned out light bulbs in the house

Chapter 8
Everyone in Your Life Is Affected

"If at some point you don't ask yourself, 'What have I gotten myself into?' then you're not doing it right." Roland Gau

In this chapter, we broaden the scope of the caregiver contract to include more than the primary family caregiver and caree.

The informal, unspoken contract you have with your spouse, children, siblings, friends, and others is affected by caregiving. The foundational principles required to co-create a new caregiver contract works the same way with these relationships. Doing the work on emotions, boundaries, and hard conversations keeps the relationship healthy. Asking for help and creating a support network keeps the caregiver sane.

What follows are four stories of very different families. These families were not intentional about co-creating a new relationship contract, nor do the stories necessarily have all the components discussed in this book. But you will see how dealing with emotions, hard conversations, setting boundaries, saying "yes" to help, and creating a support network shows up in their lives.

Maggie and Ben's story

Maggie and Ben are college sweethearts, together for 46 years and married for 42 years; they have three children and three grandchildren. Expectations set in childhood set the stage for Maggie as her mother's caregiver.

Maggie is an only child, and Ben has one younger sibling. As an only child, there was the unspoken expectation that she would care for her parents as they grew older. As a little girl, Maggie's grandmothers, various aunts, and cousins lived with them during hard times. The longest living arrangement with additional relatives was about five years. For Maggie, having someone move in with her in order to help is the family norm. It was natural for her to fall into the caregiver role when her mother needed her.

The caregiving dynamic in Ben's family was different. As a child, his nana and pop lived with them until they became ill, upon which they moved into a facility.

Sometimes we are thrust into the caregiving role, and sometimes we can see it coming. What can be universal are feelings of resentment and anger—particularly when we feel we were given no choice in taking on the role of caregiver.

Maggie's dad was diagnosed in the late 1980s with lung cancer. He died three months later, and her mother came to live with them. She functioned well on her own for about a year.

Maggie describes her marriage as traditional but sees her parents' marriage as Victorian. She sees this as the main reason Ben and her father decided her mother would move in with them without consulting her.

"I had no say in Mom coming here to live. It was a decision made by my dad and my husband. Right off the bat, I felt resentment because I was never consulted. It's not that I didn't want to care for Mom, but I knew 100% of her care would fall on me. I was angry with my husband and resentful for a lot of years that the decision was taken out of my hands. I would have taken care of Mom anyway, but I was never given the choice. The best way I can describe it is that I did not like the idea that it happened TO me, not WITH me."

Maggie's mother came to live with her when they had three children under ten years old. It required renovations to their home so she would have her own bedroom and bathroom. The first year she was still active and could take care of herself. However, used to the marriage relationship contract she had with Maggie's father, her mother was more interested in Maggie doing everything for her. Maggie kept those pieces of her parents' contract. *"I felt a deep obligation to not rock Mom's boat after the loss of Dad and her home."*

During the five years in Maggie and Ben's home, her mother developed neck and throat cancer, needing specialized trach care.

When her mother progressed to the point that she would stop breathing during the night, Maggie fell into the pattern of sleeping on the couch because it was more convenient to be close if she needed help.

When you take on the role of caregiver and have a family, chances are you are not ready for the impact it will have on all the relationships in your life. In the tornado of caring for someone that is ill and caring for your family, it is important to take a step back and evaluate what is going on with these relationships. That awareness allows you to co-create a new relationship contract and deal with emotions. If you don't, you may find yourself in the same place Maggie and Ben found themselves.

It was during these five years, when 92% of Maggie's energy was focused on caring for her mom, that Maggie and Ben's relationship contract drastically changed. Ben took greater responsibility for their children and was resentful of being completely responsible for taking them to practices and play dates. Because Mom could not be left alone, if one of them wanted to get away, they did it separately.

"The result was an absolute disconnect in our marriage. After my mother died, it took us about three years to come back to common ground. We had to figure out how to be a couple again; we had to decide if we still WANTED to be a couple. It was hard. Our new norm was doing our own thing, and it became one of the biggest sticking points of our marriage.

"At the time, I shared the struggles we were going through with no one—not even friends from college who I get together with several times a year. Still, I wouldn't change the way I handled that time in my life. These friends were my oasis, and I didn't want to waste time talking about what was going on at home."

Hard conversations become even more difficult once there is a disconnect in a relationship.

Not long after Maggie's mother died, Ben was diagnosed with a progressive auto-immune disease. It's gotten worse over time, and there is no way to predict the trajectory. At that time, they were still working through their marital disconnect. And because they had gotten in the habit of going their separate ways, Ben was initially reluctant to share details on his diagnosis. Maggie's initial reaction was denial and "I can't do this again." Fortunately, Ben's disease has been slow-moving. But Maggie knows it feels like the sword of Damocles hanging over his head as he tries to keep up with tinkering with cars, his passion. *"I know he finds it frustrating, and he will talk to me about it, which is a huge move forward. I listen and don't try to give him advice. I let him vent his frustrations and let him know I would be happy to help in any way I can, validating his experience without trying to fix it."*

Every time we take on the caregiver role, we learn something and have an opportunity to handle things differently. You don't know what you don't know.

Three years ago Ben's mother had a stroke. This time around it was different. Ben asked Maggie how she would feel about having his mother move in with them. *"I had a much greater say in my mother-in-law coming to live with us. But I have to admit I resent her being here. Ben doesn't feel the same sense of responsibility that I do to her. I feel badly about leaving her for too long, but at the same time I can't be her only social outlet. My resentment comes out of frustration because there are things she could do for herself like socialize at a senior center, but she refuses to go. I can't make her scrub the shower, but she could wipe down the bathroom counter, and she won't. I wind up doing it because it's easier."*

Because Maggie's mother-in-law is so emotionally needy, they find themselves sneaking out to have alone time. *"It's kind of like being a teenager again. Sneaking around is adventurous and fun; it's binding us together and making us stronger as a couple."*

Caregiving and health issues have a way of helping us see that the way things used to be, the expectations we have for one another, may need to change, opening the door to new or different boundaries.

Within the last two years Maggie received a cancer diagnosis, and Ben has been a trooper right by her side. Both Maggie and Ben are great socializers and over the last couple of years have learned how to let go of some of the same things. *"Last Thursday Ben asked me if I was up for hosting a Tiki bar night. He said, 'Tell me if you don't feel up to it.' Whereas before my not wanting to host and socialize would have been a big deal for him, he realizes that my energy level since the treatments is just not the same."*

When Maggie's mom was living with them, their children were young and she was home with them, despite all the time spent with her mother. *"Our kids knew Nana lived with us and wasn't well, but they didn't understand the gravity of the situation. They didn't put together that the outcome would not be a happy one. It's different with my mother-in-law. As adults, our relationship is more than a parent/child relationship; we are friends as well. My daughter and son-in-law will bring the great-grandchildren over to see her and take her out for breakfast. My son and daughter-in-law will do the same. My other daughter and son-in-law live too far away to support us as often, but make sure to keep in contact. I know her living here affects my children. They are my fallback, and I feel guilty for asking them to come over and make them do what I feel is our job. Ben does recognize when I need a break from being with her, and he will take her out for the day. It really helps.*

"We learned from our experience with my mother how to approach caregiving differently with my mother-in-law. In forging this new experience, Ben and I are staying strong as a couple. I also learned that you can find 750 different ways to place guilt on yourself in this experience. It isn't necessary so cut yourself a break. Find ways to make it easy on yourself. Now, instead of not sharing what is going on, I will vent to my friends. They've known our family for years, even my mother-in-law. They get it, they don't judge, and, in the sharing, we can laugh about the experiences."

In this story you see how Maggie struggled with resentment and anger because she was not given a choice about caregiving. If we don't name, claim, and work to change our emotions, it puts stress on our relationships. An honest discussion when Maggie's mother moved in may have resulted in an adjusted relationship contract right then, allowing Ben and Maggie's marriage to bypass difficult years. The bottom line is: Everyone makes the best decisions they can when caught in the tornado of caregiving, and if we're lucky, we learn something for the next go-round.

Kara and Michael's story

Kara is her husband's primary caregiver. Michael has Lou Gehrig's disease (ALS), and the entire family is living with his diagnosis. Their two children were age one and four years when he was diagnosed; they are five and eight years old now. Kara has no historical caregiving experience other than her grandmother's presence in her life, a person living with Alzheimer's. Caregiving for a spouse, especially a young one when there are children in the house, adds some unique challenges.

Kara and Michael did not have the many years of a relationship contract that my parents did when I became Mom's caregiver. In many ways, they were still developing how to be in relationship with one another and how to be parents when Michael was diagnosed. Because of the progression of Michael's disease, they are constantly co-creating their caregiver contract.

"Being Michael's main caregiver adds a different layer to our relationship because we are no longer equals. Before he was diagnosed, we shared responsibility for the kids and the house. Now more and more gets put on my plate."

Michael had about a year before the mobility limitations caused by ALS began to take a toll on the family. Today he requires help eating, grooming, and toileting. *"I truly am his hands and feet. But the most difficult has been his loss of speech. Understanding him can be difficult and can be beyond stressful for both of us. When I can't hear him over the kids or he can't carry on a conversation comfortably in a social situation, it leaves everyone uncomfortable."*

Kara is well aware of the importance of self-care and of keeping positive under the constant stress of caregiving.

Kara and Michael are currently facing two main caregiving challenges. The biggest challenge for Kara is the lack of time. *"Time is a scarce commodity. It's why I left my corporate job and why I became a Certified Caregiving Consultant™. In starting this business, my intent is to help other families living with ALS, particularly those with young children. The additional flexibility of consulting will give me more time for my husband as his needs increase and more time for our children. And I am determined to set aside time for myself. Getting out of the house and spending time with friends is critical to my self-care. I also know that I must make time to exercise both for my mental health and to stay fit. My husband has 75 lbs on me. I need the physical strength to transfer him, and exercise is a great stress reliever.*

"I have learned over the last couple of years how important it is for me to set my intentions on how I want to be as a caregiver.

Keeping a gratitude journal helps my mindset, which, in turn, helps me keep the big picture in mind and let stuff go. If I don't let other people help, if I spiral down into a negative mindset, my attitude crumbles and then everyone's attitude crumbles. I'm learning how to give myself grace in this situation."

Coming to terms with expectations that must be adjusted due to an illness is not easy—especially when expectations will need to be continually adjusted downwards.

The second biggest challenge is Michael's physical limitations and how it has changed the way they can be together in relationship as a family. *"Up until two years ago, Michael still had mobility. That first year there was not a notable difference from a day-to-day standpoint. As his mobility worsened, it has been hard to give up expectations about how I envisioned our life as a family. I'd love to go camping, biking, or be spontaneous with any physical activity. We used to take trips when the kids were younger; now it takes a ton of extra work to get out of the house.*

"Even getting out for simple activities is problematic—never mind going to the beach with sand and his wheelchair or getting out in the snow and ice. The wheelchair and the weather limit what we can do. Even going out to dinner is challenging. Michael needs help eating, the kids need help, and conversation in loud environments is nonexistent. It's hard on Michael because he can't go to environments he used to love. It takes a lot of mental preparation on my part to get beyond the complicated factors of getting out of the house."

It often takes extra effort as a caregiver to support your loved one's need for independence and quality of life. At the same time, we must come to terms with so many losses: ours, our carees, and those of our children as well.

Despite these losses, Michael has found a quality of life through technology that Kara fully supports. *"Thank God for technology. Michael is technically savvy so he has put together the Clue board game on his computer, and we can play the game as a family. We'll have dance parties at the house, and Michael DJ's using his computer and Bluetooth. We'll have company over to the house or go see friends. In good weather he'll come out to the kids' baseball games. On his computer he's designed a banner and tee shirts for our family picnic. Everything he does, he does for the kids. He has even created a 3D layout of our church expansion. Being able to contribute in this way helps him feel like there is still quality to his life.*

"I think the biggest loss for me is that we probably would have had another child. To have that choice taken away because future demands can't be predicted is hard. Learning to let go of things I see my friends able to do is hard as well. I have to acknowledge the loss and allow myself to grieve. What helps is to work on a mindset that gives me energy. Being able to go out with friends, take some time to read, and getting out of the house with the kids when I take them to their sport events is relaxing to me."

"I know this is hard on the children. Our eight-year-old tells me he remembers when Daddy would throw him up in the air. I don't know if that is a memory or he has seen pictures. My oldest at eight years old has become more independent and responsible. He's always been a good kid, but now he's taken on helping his younger brother."

Help comes in many forms and from many places. Sometimes it comes from our family of origin, and sometimes it comes from our family of choice. The most important thing Kara has learned is to ask for and say "yes" to help.

Kara and Michael have a paid caregiver that comes in twice a week for light housecleaning, basic grooming, and medication management. And they've learned to outsource some of the house upkeep like mowing the lawn.

"My parents and Michael's parents are our backup. They will call or come out and stop to check on him if I'm taking time to be with friends in the evening or on a weekend. We both have siblings but none of them really help with his care. It is anxiety producing for all of us when someone other than a select few people help him eat and drink. They don't know the tricks that I know to keep him from choking. My sisters will bring a meal over and help with the kids, but it's different with Michael's family. Michael and his brother are very different people. They did not have a close relationship growing up, and that has carried over into adulthood and his illness. And his sister has too much going on in her own life to help.

"I'm fortunate to have good friends. I've not had the experience

of friends falling off the face of the earth when hard times hit. Nor do I feel like I've had to renegotiate my social contract with them. Most seem to understand or are willing to ask questions out of a sincere place, never judgmentally. In fact, we've had phenomenal support. One friend takes a load of the kids' laundry each week and brings it back folded with special treats on top. Others will take the kids so I can get things done at home or for work. It's been harder on Michael; more of his friends have fallen off. They will text but don't come to visit. I wonder if they are fearful of what to expect."

Co-creating a new caregiver relationship contract in reaction to ever-changing circumstances can exacerbate differences in styles, personalities, and habits. But open and honest hard conversations help pave the way.

There have been a lot of subtle changes in their relationship that happened along the way, and these changes occurred without much discussion. Part of it is the progression of the disease. When your partner can do less and less, the spouse takes on more and more. And yet, they are still in relationship as a married couple. Personalities and habits still come into play. Figuring out how to deal with those things that drive one crazy when one's partner was healthy becomes part of co-creating a new contract.

"Our roles in this relationship get turned upside down every day. Much of the role changes we have fallen into because we've had no choice.

"Our expectations have had to change as our roles changed. Michael has always been a perfectionist. This is not an outgrowth of his diagnosis, nor is his verbal blunt tone. This part of his personality has always set me off so his being ill didn't change that dynamic immediately.

"The first time he asked me to clip his nails, we could have gotten divorced over it. We had such different goals. I wanted to be done with this task, and he wanted it done the way he would have done it. It's been a challenge for both of us to be open to each other's perspective. We've both had to learn to let things go and pick our battles. Michael has learned that I do better when I understand the why behind his request and why it's important that I do it right now. For example, if he tells me that he can't move his arm, which means he can't move his joystick, I understand the urgency so I hear it as a request, not a demand. I always try to

acknowledge and thank him for explaining because now it makes sense to me, and I appreciate his modifying his communication style.

"I also have to remind myself that Michael is still the children's father so I need to respect his views on the house rules and the disciplinary aspect of parenting. It's an interesting parenting dynamic that really would be the same even without the ALS. As more and more has fallen on me, I don't have the energy or time to supervise the boys in the same way as Michael wants to see. We do have rules and expectations for them but if I need a break, I'm more likely to say, 'yeah, you can watch the movie.' But their father then decides, 'You have to clean up the playroom before you can watch the movie.' So now I have to monitor the cleaning up process, and that can cause some tension."

Owning your emotions and being intentional about creating a positive mindset ripples down to everyone in relationship with the caregiver and caree.

"A big part of my adjustment has been working on a positive mindset. When I'm crabby and grumpy, it reflects on him. If I am venting because he wants me to do something when I need to be doing something else to keep all the balls in the air, I try to make sure he understands that it's not him; it's the stupid disease. But then he'll tell me he feels worthless, and that is extra guilt on me. He already feels badly; my venting doesn't help the situation.

"And really, a part of me gets mad that I CAN'T get mad at him. I miss our ability to have those stupid fights all married couples have. It used to feel good to release some tension and frustration by a good fight, and the making up can be wonderful. But we made the choice to stick this out when we married so we're working through it.

"I think the biggest lesson I've learned is that it is important to keep a vision of who I want to be as Michael's caregiver and his spouse. I'm learning to take a step back if I need to in order to be that person. When I am positive, it encourages him. And I recognize how important it is for me to help him keep up his quality of life and help him continue to contribute to our immediate and extended family. Technology has been an important way for him to contribute. I know all that he does, he does for me and our children."

In this story you see how Kara and Michael are constantly renegotiating their caregiver relationship contract due to changes in

Michael's health. Kara understands the importance of self-care and how asking for and saying "yes" to help with Michael, the children, and their home are part of that self-care. Kara's willingness to own her emotions and her hard work on maintaining a positive mindset make a difference in Michael and their relationship. Her support of Michael's place in the family and his quality of life choices help keep their relationship healthy and working as a team.

Rachel's story

Secrets, especially long-standing ones, ripple down through the generations with an impact that is felt for years. Secrets are the opposite of having the hard, honest conversations needed to co-create a caregiver relationship contract.

Rachel is married with two children. She has spent her entire career in health care and now works for a nonprofit in this industry. She attributes her healthcare career to growing up in a family in which the environment was always one of sickness. The youngest of three children and the only daughter, Rachel's middle brother lived with cystic fibrosis (CF). At that time people in general, and her family in particular, were very quiet about illness, especially that of a son. Her brother's CF journey was never shared with Rachel or her older brother, and she suspects her father did not know the entire story as well. Rachel's brother was 20 years old when he died, Rachel was 14 years old, and her older brother was 24 years old.

The loss of her middle brother to CF broke their family apart. The secrecy around her brother's illness and the lack of trust for sharing the why for all the hospitalizations and respiratory treatments affected everyone. The lack of conversation around illness and the inability to express feelings resulted in her older brother moving away from the family. He still has unresolved anger, and the sibling relationship between he and Rachel is fractured.

Unspoken expectations often go unchallenged. Without recognizing and discussing expectations, you cannot set boundaries. Indeed, you may not even recognize a boundary is needed.

Rachel's parents had a very traditional marriage in which her mom took care of all her dad's needs. When her mom became ill with cardiovascular disease, it was expected by everyone, including Rachel, that she would be Mom's primary caregiver.

Over the 13 years as her mother's caregiver, Rachel made her mom the priority both as her caregiver and advocate.

"There was always this gnawing sense of continued responsibility to make sure Mom was happy, as active in her life as she could be, and that she saw her grandchildren. Once she became debilitatingly ill, I became her CEO of medical care. My life became all about making sure she had everything she needed. At times caring for Mom was really difficult. There came a point when I had to diaper my mother, and I thought, 'If she ever knew I was doing this for her, she would be out of her mind.' My mother didn't want the traditional female role for me. She never taught me how to cook; she wanted me to do better.

"Dad never became involved in Mom's caregiving. When you're the daughter, you're the daughter, and you just take care of your mother. But I felt alone, was exhausted, and stressed. It is difficult as the caregiver to take care of yourself. This is why in my work I stress that caregivers learn to take care of themselves."

Taking over someone else's contract without negotiating changes can bring up feelings of anger and resentment. In this case, Rachel and her father took the opportunity to grow closer.

After her mother died, Rachel became her father's caregiver, but not in a medical sense. Initially, the pattern of the females in his life taking on complete responsibility for him started with his mother, continued with Rachel's mom and, after her mother died, *"Dad expected his contract with my mother to continue with me. It was as if her name came off it and my name was inked in."*

As Dad's caregiver while he was still healthy, Rachel took responsibility for his day-to-day concerns, finances, shopping, and social calendar. When he became ill, she took over his medical needs as well. Taking on day-to-day responsibility for her father while he was still in good health did change their social contract. As a child, he was distant, and they were not close. *"It was hard in the beginning. Where there was love and a happy emotional connection with my mother, I had anger, resentment, and frustration when I became responsible for my father. It felt as if I had no choice. That caring for him was an obligation because I was doing what my mother would want me to do. And yet, our relationship grew; we became a team. Sharing time with him grocery shopping, taking him out to eat, and taking him anywhere else he needed to go allowed us to establish a different relationship."*

Rachel did opt to have the help of professional caregivers with her father. She did find the process of working with caregivers frustrating and went through many of them in a short period of time.

When caregiving is your primary focus, it affects the entire family. Siblings who check out, don't help, and are toxic make it even more difficult.

Starting with caregiving for her mother, Rachel feels that she put her children and husband after her mother, and there are so many feelings because of it. *"It was very hard because it was just me. It didn't have to be that way. My brother could have been involved, but he chose distance. In many ways my brother was a hindrance emotionally. We didn't see him for a few years, and then when he did come back, Dad fell, and everything went downhill."*

Rachel's husband, on the other hand, was a help. He took an active role in caring for her dad while he was still healthy. *"He would take Dad food shopping, pay his bills, but even though he was a big support to my dad, they never did develop a strong relationship. I think the only person I ever saw my father show emotion for was his grandson. He did not have a relationship with my daughter. He and my son shared a love of sports so they watched football and baseball games together."*

Circumstances were different but Rachel and her husband, like Maggie and Ben, were able to work through the strain caregiving put on their marriage.

"In the beginning, caring for my mom had a negative effect on my marriage. We were able to work through it because when his dad passed, Ben took over responsibility for his younger sister. Later he was his mom's caregiver so when I became my mom's caregiver, what I was doing was natural to him."

"Being Mom's caregiver also had a negative effect on my children. My obligation was to my mother. Even though I was a good mother, my priorities shifted. "

"Because of my work, the relationship contract between my husband and I already had him involved and helping with the children and house. As my caregiving contract for Mom expanded, my husband took up the slack."

"Dad was an only child, and Mom was one of five sisters and brothers, but when it came to her care, it was easier to take it all on

than to deal with the criticism of how I was handling things. When someone is not in the day to day, they can't see it. And of course, Dad as an only meant I was it for him."

Dealing with emotions around caregiving does not stop when caregiving ends.

Because both parents are gone now, Rachel does feel the loss of her brother as part of her family of origin. But it was her brother's choice to disappear so she has moved beyond the loss.

Today she is working on putting herself first. *"I feel like I lost myself in this process. I don't even know what RACHEL wants and needs yet. One of the hardest parts is there was no time to develop friendships. My childhood friend, a sister really, passed early on from cancer. I never had the time to invest in me or friendships. You give up a lot and get angry for it. I'm still working through the anger."*

In this story we learn how secrets can affect families for generations and cause a rift between siblings that is exacerbated by caregiving. But the caregiving journey offers an opportunity to heal relationships as well. When caregiving ends, we often wonder, "Who am I if I'm no longer a caregiver?"

The Quigley sisters
"No one ever warned us about having parents!"

John, Colleen's husband

Four sisters have banded together to care for their aging parents. Like most sibling caregivers, one of them takes the lead. Unlike many family caregiving teams, they are not bound by birth order in their caregiving roles. The role each sister plays on Team Quigley capitalizes on individual strengths and takes into account family circumstances.

Anna is the oldest, then Colleen, Brianna, and Ailis. Three of the four siblings are married with children. Growing up in a large close-knit Irish family has made their transition to caregiving easier than other families may find it.

Caregiving is not new to this team of sisters. The spouses of Anna, Colleen, and Ailis have either been involved in caregiving for their parents or are currently involved. They point out that the family dynamics of caregiving for in-laws are different than the dynamics with their own parents.

When asked "Who is the primary caregiver?" there was a quick and unanimous chorus: "Colleen is the boss." In fact, as Anna explains it, "Colleen is more like a crossing guard, making sure everyone is where they need to be and that they get their safely." And Colleen is quick to say that she could not do it without them. If there is a major decision to be made, the sisters, along with their parents, make it as a team.

Colleen became the de facto primary caregiver because she lives ten minutes away from their parents.

"Anna and Ailis live 40 minutes away, Ailis has young children, and Brianna works. So it makes sense for me to be the primary caregiver. I can run over and help Mom shower and then head back home, whereas for the others it takes a lot more planning and work to help on a daily basis."

Caregiving, in which you support a primary caregiver and are not personally involved in the day-to-day activities, does not prepare you for the all-consuming role of hands on caregiving. Nor does it prepare you for how the relationship changes and the need to co-create a caregiver contract arises.

But over the last year, they have been involved in caregiving with a capital C as their parents struggled with their health. Their mother has lived with a chronic disease for years, and their father was her caregiver with the help of his daughters. Dad was holding his own, then over the last couple of years he lost enough of his eyesight that he gave up driving, some other health concerns worsened, and a recent fall landed him in the hospital and required surgery. Over the last six months the family has been in the tornado of caregiving focused on supporting Dad in order for him to regain his health.

"The turning point for Dad was when he lost his eyesight and could not drive. He is so self-aware and practical. He knew he could not drive so he gave it up on his own. It depressed him to no end, but he handled it well. I'm so proud of him. He can accept help much more easily than Mom. When he needs help, he is gracious about it. But even so, when he first came home from rehab and needed so much help getting around, he was horrified. And he feels bad about taking us away from our families to help. He has said to us, 'I take

up so much time from you guys. I feel bad.' For us, when the relationship you had before your loved one got sick is good, it's not a chore to help them. It's the circle of life," said Ailis.

Mom, on the other hand, struggles with asking for help. She doesn't want to ask for it, and she doesn't like to feel needy.

It is difficult to not "parent your parent" when they put themselves in danger. A team of siblings has the ability to focus on the parent they understand best and to hand off caregiving tasks to one another.

"I'll be over there at lunch time, and Dad will sit down and let me bring him lunch. Mom, on the other hand, will move around the kitchen doing her own thing, even though I'm there to get her lunch as well. Sometimes I find myself yelling at her like she is a little kid as she maneuvers around me to get to the fridge, even though she is not safe doing it. I feel bad about screaming at her. But I have zero patience with stupid behavior, hers or anyone else's, and all my patience is already being used up on the important things," added Colleen.

"I have much less patience with Mom as well. I'm better dealing with Dad," said Ailis.

"I have more patience dealing with Mom and know a bit more about what she feels and wants. When Colleen and her husband went on vacation, I helped Mom shower. It was a big deal originally to get permission for Colleen to help her shower so it really threw her when I was the one helping. She had a hard time with it. I don't think it was about me; it's just that Mom has a hard time giving up control. When I had to help her, I think she had to come to grips with needing help for this very personal task all over again," explained Anna.

The division of labor between sisters happens in one of two ways. First, as the primary, Colleen gets most things done and, if help is needed, she will call on one of her sisters. The other way people take on tasks is by virtue of being on-site when an issue arises.

"If one of us is at Mom and Dad's or we are talking to them on the phone and an issue arises, we kind of get sucked into whatever is the issue of the day, which is fine. If the conversation turns to something like needing a blood test, whichever sister is at their house calls and makes an appointment for the day she knows she is

available. One day when I was there Mom mentioned she wanted to go to the hairdresser. It was urgent to Mom, and I didn't realize it. When I made the appointment, it meant coming back the next day to take Mom, which was fine. Once you commit to something, you own it," said Ailis.

Briana takes over many of the daily tasks such as unloading the dishwasher, putting clothes away, and helping Mom put her PJs on, freeing Colleen up for tasks Briana is unable to do like driving her parents to the doctors.

The transition into their caregiver roles was easy for the Quigley sisters because of their strong familial connection. But they have seen through experience with their in-laws that pressures due to caregiving can make it difficult for siblings to share tasks. Nor is it easy when parents are unwilling to accept help as well as when young children struggle with new family priorities.

Colleen and John

Colleen and John's first experience with caregiving was with his parents, and it put pressure on the sibling relationship. John and his sister approached caregiving from very different places, and they wound up having a falling-out. His advice to friends new to a caregiver situation: *"Let me tell you, just be supportive of your siblings. Don't ever criticize how they are approaching it."*

"When his mom had surgery, John was suddenly thrust into the caregiver role again. His dad died several years ago. His one brother had died, and his sister lives too far away. Now, in addition to being responsible for maintaining his mom's house, he is dealing with doctor appointments, etc. Up until about a year ago, our interaction with John's mom had been mostly social, having her to dinner, or she would join us for dinners at my parents' house. That changed in a big way. "

"Caregiving for John's parents, and now mine, hasn't really changed our relationship. When John's dad got sick years ago and he had to help him, he made the decision to take a job that was closer to home. He set boundaries when he took the job, making sure they understood that he would be leaving at five o'clock because he was not missing his kids' games. And he made sure that management understood that if his father needed him, he would leave. John gave up a bit of his career in order to be a son and a

father."

"I wonder sometimes if we both feel such a responsibility to our parents because we live in the same town, the town we grew up in. We've never gotten mad at one another for helping our parents out. I love the fact that because we live in the same town, I can run over to my parents' house, feed Dad, and be home ten minutes later. I'm not trying to make it sound easy because it's not. But it is certainly easier for me to pop over and help than for Anna or Ailis who live further away," said Colleen.

Anna and Kevin

Kevin is one of five children, and each sibling assumed the role that was natural to their skill set.

"After Kevin's father passed his mother was living alone in FL, and her health began deteriorating. With four of the siblings in NJ and one in MD, it was decided the best way to care for her would be to uproot her and bring her back to NJ. Since one sister is a nurse, she was looked upon as the expert for healthcare issues.

"Kevin's oldest sister was the natural boss so she often made the everyday care decisions. The other siblings filled in as needed—although some family members helped out more than others. Once his mother was settled in an assisted living community, the biggest challenge we had was finding time to visit with her. She wasn't thrilled with the living arrangement so providing her with company was important to the family. Caring for my mother-in-law did wind up taking Kevin away from doing things with our kids since he was trying to juggle his mom and work at the same time.

"I was able to help Kevin with his mom once she moved back to the area. And it was different when she moved back than when my children were younger. Like any in-law relationship, there were times when I was overwhelmed, and it was difficult. But when they age and need you, you forget your past complaints and focus on their current needs. I guess Kevin and I could have set boundaries in those early years, but it was important to Kevin to treat his parents well. It made him happy, and I love him so I did what I had to do," said Anna.

Ailis and Sean

Ailis's husband is an only child; his parents had him late in life. Because of that, Sean's family dynamics were very different from the Quigley family.

"Sean's relationship with his parents is different than mine. Trying to get them to accept help has been awkward. His dad was his mother's caregiver until she passed not long ago. His mom had Alzheimer's, and we offered to help them in several ways. We wanted to hire a cleaning lady for them because his dad was determined to keep his mom at home. We live so far away and our kids are so young that what we could do physically was limited. And honestly, given some emotional distance in our relationship, the appetite for going up there was not huge. Now Sean's dad is alone; he just had a knee replacement, and he is still refusing help. It was a fight for a full year to try and ensure that proper legal documents were in place. I'm still not sure his dad actually completed them. As it is, we see him about once a month for a social visit, but I feel guilty that we are not doing enough," said Ailis.

Sibling caregivers that support one another, ensure each is taking time for self-care, and have a support network outside of the family come through this experience stronger.

As you would expect, caring for aging parents has had an impact on the lives of their children, their friendships, and work life. But each sister makes room for self-care, and they support one another in those goals.

"Just today I got a massage, a Christmas gift from Brianna. I consider it a luxury that I don't have to work and that my job can be as the primary caregiver for our parents. In some ways, there is no guilt because my job is shopping and cooking for my family and my parents and making sure they are cared for. I don't carry around a lot of angst. Our kids are older now, and they have really risen to the occasion while we have had to step up to help with my parents. If they are home from college and not working, they always join us at my parents' house for Sunday dinner.

"John and I still manage to see our high school friends. We host dinner parties or go out to dinner with them. Our friends are a nice support group for this stage in our lives. We talk about our parents getting older and how we are all in the same boat. We talk about how we still have good years ahead of us and how we want to live them. We are more aware of the limits that declining health will put on us. Our daughter just had a semester abroad, and I was so stressed at the thought of leaving to go visit her. But my husband

said, 'We're going. We will find a way to make it work.' My sisters helped us make it work. I'm so glad we did it," said Colleen.

"Helping with my parents, and even with Kevin's mom, has had the biggest impact on our children, not on us. Caregiving took away time from the kids, and there were late dinners or times when they fixed their own dinner. They really moved from the number one spot to number two, which was an adjustment. Fortunately, like Colleen's kids, mine are older and have really risen to the occasion while Dad's been sick. It helps to let go of some of your own expectations.

"As for me, once I get over the guilt about everything Colleen is doing, I make time to ensure I get my run in or get to the gym. Even if I'm at Mom and Dad's helping, I get my run in. Taking my sisters golfing has also been an outlet for us.

"Caregiving didn't change our social life that much. For Kevin and me, family is our first social circle. We deferred friendships over the years to be with family. That helped when Dad got so sick. It was nothing for me to give up Saturday nights to help with his feeding tube. And it was respite for Colleen," said Anna.

Everyone, even young children, have expectations and boundaries. Balancing a young family with work and caregiving means resetting our own expectations and setting boundaries.

"Our kids are young enough that most of our social interactions happen on the playground. Not getting to see our friends had less of an impact because our focus is on the children. When Dad was really sick, Sean had to pick up the slack with our kids. On Sunday morning I'd say goodbye to them and say, 'I'll see you when I see you.' Even at that, in the January through May time frame, Colleen and Anna took the brunt of the weekend stuff. I think I did one Saturday overnight and feeding for Dad.

"The kids are too young to really know what was going on. In the middle of all the medical stuff with Dad, when I would be away for hours at time, they would be with the babysitter. One day when I came home, my oldest son said to me, 'I need to talk to you privately. I needed you when I got home, and you weren't here. You were with Grandpa again.' I felt horrible. What he needed wasn't a big deal, but it was a big deal to him.

"In the midst of this, I do get to the gym a few times a week. I

don't get the same joy that Anna does, but it's important. I also make sure to get to book club every six weeks; that is an important outlet for me. And Sean and I will go away for a weekend for the first time in a few weeks, with the help of my nieces during the day and Anna watching them at night.

"Through all this, my business did take a hit during Dad's health crisis. I had a large project lined up and could only take on half of it. Fortunately, I had an established relationship with the client. I was able to tell them why I could only do half the project. I let them know what I could do, what my limits were. And I had to turn down another big project. Any space beyond my primary client went to my dad," Ailis said.

In this story, you see how healthy family relationships can weather the tornado of caring for aging parents and grow stronger through the journey. It is not easy to form a tight family caregiving team and support one another, but it can be done and is well worth negotiating new sibling relationship contracts.

Lessons learned from this book and these four families

1. Feeling like caregiving is thrust upon you without your consent can lead to resentment and a breakdown in communications.
   a. Other family members may need to take over roles they are unprepared to take on.
   b. Stress affects caregiving.

2. Becoming a team with your caree means letting go of past hurts.

3. Caregiving is often all-consuming, affecting relationships with your spouse and children and changing family dynamics.
   a. It helps if your spouse is or was a caregiver; they get it.

4. Caregiving can be a team sport.
   a. Other family members may need to take on roles they are unprepared to take on.

    b. When there are multiple caregivers, having one person coordinate care is a great strategy.

    c. Sibling strife in caregiving is not an automatic outcome; siblings can and do form strong teams.

    d. Play to the strengths of each member of the team.

5. It is possible to learn from each experience and decide to handle things differently and partner with your caree.

6. It can be helpful to share details about this journey with people you trust.

7. Secrets affect families and can influence caregiving, familial relationships, and the family of origin.

8. Self-care in whatever form it takes is critical.

    a. It takes work to keep a positive mindset, but it can make all the difference in the world .

    b. It is OK to let yourself grieve.

    c. When the caregiving team supports one another in self-care, everyone wins.

    d. Find your team's best method of communication. It can be phone calls on a regular basis, group texts, or a closed Facebook group.

9. It is hard to give up long held expectations.

Conclusion

This book is written to give you insight and clarity into your caregiver/caree relationship. Clarity requires reflection, self-awareness, and honesty—the first three pillars needed to frame a caregiver relationship contract. Without these elements, change is not possible. Without change, we can't co-create a loving and supportive caregiver relationship contract.

Framing a relationship as a contract can initially seem cold. My clients and I have found that framing it like this allows us to take a step back from all the emotions involved in caregiving. And this step back is the fourth pillar for clarity.

Clarity doesn't happen overnight. It comes in fits and starts as you careen from one caregiving crisis to another. It comes in the quiet of the night when you can't sleep. It comes in the middle of an argument.

With each new insight it becomes easier to see where boundaries are needed, and expectations must be reset. It becomes easier to admit that you need help and then take the steps to seek it out. You will recognize more quickly when it is time to have a difficult conversation with your loved one and have the courage to engage them in that conversation.

Caregiving is hard, and there will be people in your life who don't understand your new priorities. This is why creating a support network is so important. It doesn't matter if your support network is online or friends from your childhood. People that get it, people that understand, are part of your self-care and just as important as the trip to your gym, book club, a nap, or a good novel.

Caregiving changes life for everyone in your life, not just you and your caree. The tools in this book are meant to be applied to all your relationships. Children like Ailis's young son are not going to be able to negotiate a new contract with you in the same way that an adult (even one acting like a child) can. There is a resource in the back of the book that can help you have some of those hard conversations with the young people in your life.

If you are reading this book and are thinking, "I'm not cut out to be a caregiver," that's OK. Not everyone is or wants to be. Clarity on this truth gives you the ability to make different plans for your loved one. And those plans may well salvage the relationship.

Finally, I'm going to ask you to take a few things with you when you close this book's cover:

- ♥ Please don't "parent your parent."
- ♥ The words you use and the way you present change matters.
- ♥ Emotions need to be dealt with. Name them, claim them, and then change them.
- ♥ Take respite where you can find it.
- ♥ Laugh at yourself or the situation with your loved one and caregiving peeps.
- ♥ Be kind to yourself; give yourself grace.
- ♥ Be well.

Resources

Advocacy groups

AARP

www.aarp.org

Along with advocating for seniors, this AARP website has an abundance of rich resources for caregivers. As you navigate through the site, look for the caregiving resource center (www.aarp.org/caregiving). It has tools, tips, and worksheets to help you on the journey.

National Patient Advocate Foundation (NAPF)

https://www.npaf.org/

The National Patient Advocate Foundation is the advocacy affiliate of the Patient Advocate Foundation. Their mission is to represent the patient voice of the patient and the collective needs of the community. Staff and volunteers work at the local, regional, and national level to promote access to affordable, quality health care for people with chronic, debilitating, or life-threatening illnesses.

RIP Medical Debt

https://www.ripmedicaldebt.org/

This 501(c)(3) charity has abolished $584 million in medical debt for about 240,000 Americans. Your donations are used to purchase debt at pennies on the dollar, and using data analysis they locate the medical debt that is most crucially in need of relief and forgive it. Those helped are no longer obligated to pay even a cent with no adverse consequences.

Publications

Atul Gawande

https://www.amazon.com/Being-Mortal-Medicine-What-Matters-ebook/dp/B00JCW0BCY

A practicing surgeon reveals the struggles of his profession, its limitations, and its failures when it comes to the realities of aging and death. Through research and personal stories, he pulls the cover back on the false hopes and treatments doctors and nursing homes too often fall back on at the end of life. He shows that the goal for all of us—patient, family, and doctors—is not a good death but a good life all the way to the end.

Cathy Sikorski, Esq.

https://cathysikorski.com/

"Who Moved My Teeth? Preparing for Self, Loved Ones & Caregiving" by this author is an excellent resource. Cathy has a 25-year career as a caregiver for seven different family members and friends, not to mention a career in Elder Law. She writes with humor and grace about the topics that most of us gnash our teeth on such as Medicare, Medicaid, insurance companies, doctor offices, all the legal and financial paperwork that needs to be in place—the list goes on. The advice is easily understood and spot on. If you pick up this book and only read the chapters "The Seven Dwarfs of Hidden Symptoms" (i.e., UTIs) and "For God's Sake Stop Paying Those Medical Bills!" then your money is well spent.

"How to Say It to Seniors®: Closing the Communication Gap with Our Elders" by David Solie, M.S., P.A.

This book helped me understand why mom is often not as task focused as I am, which can be very frustrating. Even more importantly, it helped me understand why mom holds onto control so tightly. And that the language I use, statements like: "You should, you must," has her digging in her heels.

Blogs and websites for caregivers

Advocate for Mom and Dad

www.advocateformomanddad.com @advocatemomdad

The author's blog is written to educate and serve as a resource for adult children of aging parents on caregiving concerns.

AARP Caregiving Take Care Blog

http://blog.aarp.org/tag/takecare; @AmyGoyer

This blog contains personal stories by Amy Goyer and others, information, and practical tips.

AlzAuthors

https://alzauthors.com/; @alzAuthors

A website and blog dedicated to the most comprehensive collection of books and blogs about Alzheimer's. There are more than 200 authors and hundreds of inspirational stories on this website.

Caregiving.com

www.caregiving.com; @caregiving

This is one of the first websites in existence for caregivers. Founded over 20 years ago by Denise Brown, the information on it is written by and for caregivers. There are online chats for caregivers, blogs by caregivers, opportunities for learning how to create a business from your caregiving experience, and much more.

Caregiving Advice for All Ages and Stages

www.caregivingadvice.com; @MichelleSeitzer

Created by Michelle Seitzer, this site offers resources, advice, and hope for all caregivers. Mother of a special needs child, this site welcomes you to the big blue couch for conversation, connection, and compassion.

Daily Caring

https://dailycaring.com/

This website researches and compiles the practical tips, advice, personal stories, and resources for caregiving and aging. Their sources are well known such as Forbes, The New York Times, Next Avenue, and others.

Daughterhood

www.Daughterhood.org; @daughterhood

Created by Anne Tumlinson, founder of Daughterhood Circles, Anne has spent her entire career working in government doing policy research and has consulted with nursing homes, assisted living providers, and home care companies to improve how America delivers and pays for care of our aging loved ones. Daughterhood.org's mission is to support and build confidence in women who are managing their parents' care.

Taking Care of Grandma
https://takingcareofgrandma.com/; @takingcareofgma
Rachel Hiles, a millennial caregiver, shares practical caregiving advice learned from her experience taking care of her grandma.

The Caregivers' Living Room
https://www.donnathomson.com/; @Thomsod
Donna Thomson is a caregiver, author, and activist. She is the mother of two grown children, one who happens to have severe cerebral palsy and medical complexity. Donna is a board director of Kids Brain Health Network and is a leader and instructor in family engagement in health research. She also teaches families how to advocate for care at The Advocacy School and at Huddol.com.

The Thriving Caregiver
https://thethrivingcaregiver.com/
Kristen Roden is caregiver to her husband who has ALS and mother to two young sons.

Next Avenue
https://www.nextavenue.org/; @NextAvenue
Contributors to this website write on issues of health, money, work and purpose, living, caregiving, and technology. It is one of my go-to sources for information.

Your GPS Doc
https://yourgpsdoc.com/; @NRochesterMD
Nicole Rochester, M.D., is a board-certified physician and Clinical Assistant Professor with over two decades of experience teaching and practicing medicine. Nicole founded Your PGS Doctor after she witnessed the disjointed healthcare system from the other side of the stethoscope as her late father's caregiver. A physician expert on healthcare navigation, Nicole is a patient and family caregiver advocate, speaker, author, and blogger.

Caregiver support

Area Agencies on Aging

www.eldercare.gov

Local agencies will help you find services and support for seniors and their caregivers.

Caregiver Action Network

https://caregiveraction.org/

Provides education, peer support, and resources for the broad spectrum of family caregivers ranging from the parent of children with special needs to family and friends of wounded soldiers to adult children caring for aging parents.

Rosalynn Carter Institute for Caregiving (RCI)

www.rosalynncarter.org

RCI establishes local, state, national, and international partnerships committed to building quality, long-term, home and community-based services. It starts with providing caregivers with effective support to promote caregiver health, skills, and resilience with a focus on helping caregivers coping with chronic illness and disability across the lifespan.

Elizabeth Dole Foundation

https://www.elizabethdolefoundation.org/

The focus of this organization is to strengthen and empower America's military caregivers and their families through research, public awareness, and championing policy. The foundation adopts a comprehensive approach in its advocacy, working with leaders in the public, private, nonprofit, and faith communities to recognize military caregivers' service and promote their well-being.

National Alliance for Caregiving

https://www.caregiving.org/

This coalition of national organizations focuses on advancing family caregiving through research, innovation, advocacy, the development of national best practice programs, and increasing public awareness of family caregiving issues.

US Administration on Aging Elder Locator
https://eldercare.acl.gov/Public/Index.aspx
This website locates local services for older adults and their families by looking up resources in your state or zip code.

Healthcare organizations
ALS Association
www.alsa.org/ (800) 782-4747
Established in 1985, The ALS Association is the only national non-profit organization fighting ALS on every front. They lead the way in global research, providing assistance for people with ALS through a nationwide network of chapters, coordinating multidisciplinary are through certified clinical care centers and fostering government partnerships.

Alzheimer's Association
www.alz.org/ 800-272-3900
A leading voluntary health organization in Alzheimer's care, support, and research. They work to eliminate Alzheimer's disease through research and provide and enhance care and support.

Alzheimer's Foundation of America
www.alzfdn.org; 866-232-8484
Provides support, services, and education to individuals, families, and caregivers affected by Alzheimer's disease and related dementias nationwide, and funds research for better treatment and a cure.

American Cancer Society
www.cancer.org 800-22-2345
Funds and conducts research, shares expert information, and provides support.

American Heart Association
www.heart.org; 800-242-8721
An international organization dedicated to improving heart health and reducing deaths from cardiovascular diseases and stroke.

American Stroke Association
www.strokeassociation.org; 800-478-7653
Education about the types and causes of strokes along with support for individuals who have had a stroke and their caregivers.

Center for Medicaid and Medicare Services
www.cms.gov 800-633-4227
Your go-to place for information on what is covered by Medicare and Medicaid. Nursing home facilities go through an annual review qualified by a star rating of 1 to 5. The Center for Medicare and Medicaid Services (CMS) website has the latest survey ratings for post-hospital facilities at their website: https://www.medicare.gov/nursinghomecompare/search.html?
A rating of 5 from CMS is the highest rating a facility can receive. A rating below 1 will result in the facility closing.

National Institutes of Health (NIH)
https://www.nih.gov/
Funds medical research and offers a wide variety of educational and practical resources; this site links to other sites such as the National Institute on Aging.

National Institute on Aging
www.nia.nih.gov.
Here you find research information, clinical trials, and community resources including ones for seniors and caregivers.

National Parkinson Foundation
www.parkinson.org.
Provides educational information and a referral service to local resources.

Nonprofits to know about
Adopt A Senior
https://www.adopt-a-senior.org/
Founded in 2014, it provides gifts to as many seniors living in long-term care facilities as possible. They currently work with six facilities in New York and New Jersey. Each year seniors at these facility complete "Wish List" profile forms indicating items they

would like for the holidays. Friends and family, along with colleagues, then select a profile. They purchase items on the profile and wrap and tag the gift for their adopted senior. If you live too far away to donate a gift, for $50 you can adopt a senior for a year.

Hope Loves Company

https://www.hopelovescompany.org/

This nonprofit is the only one in the country with the mission to provide educational and emotional support to children and young adults who have had or have a loved one with amyotrophic lateral sclerosis (ALS) or Lou Gehrig's disease.

Cancer Hope Network

https://www.cancerhopenetwork.org/

This nonprofit provides free one-on-one emotional support to adult cancer patients and their loved ones. Each of CHN's 400+ volunteers is at least one year post-treatment or successfully undergoing maintenance therapies. They have faced more than 80 cancer types and speak 15 languages. Their volunteers offer support from diagnosis through treatment and into recovery.

Good Days

https://www.mygooddays.org/about/mission

A 501(c)(3) nonprofit organization that helps patients with certain chronic medical conditions pay their insurance co-pays.

Podcasts

Happy Healthy Caregiver

https://happyhealthycaregiver.com/podcast/

The work of Elizabeth Miller, "real" family caregivers share how to be happy and healthy while caring for others.

Colleen Kavanaugh

https://www.thelongestdance.com/podcast

Real people share their stories that explore belief, faith, and new ways of transcendent thinking. They are people who live extraordinary lives that have been transformed by the experiences of living.

Dr. Steve Silvestro

https://www.drstevesilvestro.com/how-to-tell-kids-about-a-loved-ones-illness

Dr. Steve Silvestro is an award-winning pediatrician and host of The Child Repair Guide Podcast, bringing the wisdom of the world's best child health experts directly to parents to help them navigate the challenges of raising happy, healthy kids.

Professional organizations

Aging Life Care Specialists

https://www.aginglifecare.org/

Aging Life Care™ professionals, also known as geriatric care managers, guide families about actions and decisions that ensure quality care and an optimal life for older adults

Daily Money Manager

https://secure.aadmm.com/

These professionals provide financial services to seniors and older adults, people with disabilities, and others. They will pay bills, reconcile health insurance claims, organize financial documents, serve as notary public, and make bank deposits.

National Academy of Elder Law Attorneys

www.naela.org

Resource to find local elder law attorneys.

TEDx talks

Pamela Nelson TEDxSMU

https://www.youtube.com/watch?v=5TXlZVPNWlk

When caregiving comes your way.

Amy O'Roueke TEDxOrlando

https://www.youtube.com/watch?v=4c2grKhiKEw

How to relieve caregiver stress.

Sarri Gilman

https://www.youtube.com/watch?v=rtsHUeKnkC8

Good boundaries set you free.

YouTube Videos

AARP (www.aarp.org/takinggcare) has helpful videos on a wide range of caregiving topics.

Teepa Snow YouTube channel of Teepa Snow

Teepa Snow is a dementia and Alzheimer's care expert who travels the United States and Canada educating others about dementia and the care that accompanies it. Teepa is an occupational therapist with 40y years of clinical practice. In easily understood examples, she introduces us to the best communication techniques, approach, and touch for caregivers of a person living with dementia. She brings the subject to life in a supportive and fun way. Even if you are not caregiving for a person living with dementia, you will find videos with tips for getting in and out of the car helpful.

About the Author

In 2015 life changed for Debra Hallisey. She became responsible for her disabled mother after her father's death. As she took on the roles of financial adviser, caregiver, social director—as well as her continuing role as daughter—she found herself asking "what do I do?" and "where do I start?" She brought her 25 years of experience as a consultant building and enhancing corporate training programs for Fortune 500 companies in the United States and Canada to the problem and, in the process, learned how many other people are in a similar situation caring for a parent, a sibling, a spouse, or significant other.

She has used the knowledge she has gained to develop AdvocateforMomandDad.com The site offers practical advice for caregivers and lessons learned from others on how they handle challenges on issues such as legal, financial, insurance, and caregiving.

A caregiver knowledge expert and an advocate for older adults and their families, Debra is a Certified Caregiving Consultant™ and Certified Dementia Practitioner®. She holds an M.A. in Leadership and Supervision and is currently taking additional training to become certified as a Certified Caregiving Educator (CCE) and a Certified Caregiving Facilitator (CCF).